W9-BMT-900

Student Edition

Eureka Math
Grade 2
Modules 5 & 6

Special thanks go to the Gordon A. Cain Center and to the Department of Mathematics at Louisiana State University for their support in the development of *Eureka Math*.

Published by the non-profit Great Minds

Copyright © 2015 Great Minds. No part of this work may be reproduced, sold, or commercialized, in whole or in part, without written permission from Great Minds. Non-commercial use is licensed pursuant to a Creative Commons Attribution-NonCommercial-ShareAlike 4.0 license; for more information, go to http://greatminds.net/maps/math/copyright. "Great Minds" and "Eureka Math" are registered trademarks of Great Minds.

Printed in the U.S.A.

This book may be purchased from the publisher at eureka-math.org

10 9 8 7 6 5 4 3 2

ISBN 978-1-63255-295-2

Name _____   Date _____

1. Complete each *more* or *less* statement.

    a. 10 more than 175 is _____.   b. 100 more than 175 is _____.

    c. 10 less than 175 is _____.   d. 100 less than 175 is _____.

    e. 319 is 10 more than _____.   f. 499 is 100 less than _____.

    g. _____ is 100 less than 888.   h. _____ is 10 more than 493.

    i. 898 is _____ than 998.   j. 607 is _____ than 597.

    k. 10 more than 309 is _____.   l. 309 is _____ than 319.

2. Complete each regular number pattern.

    a. 170, 180, 190, _____, _____, _____

    b. 420, 410, 400, _____, _____, _____

    c. 789, 689, _____, _____, _____, 289

    d. 565, 575, _____, _____, _____, 615

    e. 724, _____, _____, _____, 684, 674

    f. _____, _____, _____, 886, 876, 866

©2015 Great Minds. eureka-math.org
G2-M5-SE-B3-1.3.1-1.2016

3. Complete each statement.

   a. $389 \xrightarrow{+10}$ _____ $\xrightarrow{+100}$ _____   b. $187 \xrightarrow{-100}$ _____ $\xrightarrow{-10}$ _____

   c. $609 \xrightarrow{-10}$ _____ $\xrightarrow{-\underline{}} 499 \xrightarrow{+10}$ _____ $\xrightarrow{+\underline{}} 519$

   d. $512 \xrightarrow{-10}$ _____ $\xrightarrow{-10}$ _____ $\xrightarrow{+100}$ _____ $\xrightarrow{+100}$ _____ $\xrightarrow{+10}$ _____

4. Solve using the arrow way.

   a. 210 + 130 = _____

   b. 320 + _____ = 400

   c. _____ + 515 = 735

Lesson 1: Relate 10 more, 10 less, 100 more, and 100 less to addition and subtraction of 10 and 100.

©2015 Great Minds. eureka-math.org
G2-M5-SE-B3-1.3.1-1.2016

EUREKA MATH™

Name _____   Date _____

1. Complete each *more* or *less* statement.

    a. 10 more than 222 is _____.   b. 100 more than 222 is _____.

    c. 10 less than 222 is _____.   d. 100 less than 222 is _____.

    e. 515 is 10 more than _____.   f. 299 is 100 less than _____.

    g. _____ is 100 less than 345.   h. _____ is 10 more than 397.

    i. 898 is _____ than 998.   j. 607 is _____ than 597.

    k. 10 more than 309 is _____.   l. 309 is _____ than 319.

2. Complete each regular number pattern.

    a. 280, 290, _____, _____, _____, 330

    b. 530, 520, 510, _____, _____, _____

    c. 643, 543, _____, _____, _____, 143

    d. 681, 691, _____, _____, _____, 731

    e. 427, _____, _____, _____, 387, 377

    f. _____, _____, _____, 788, 778, 768

Lesson 1:   Relate 10 more, 10 less, 100 more, and 100 less to addition and
            subtraction of 10 and 100.

3

©2015 Great Minds. eureka-math.org
G2-M5-SE-B3-1.3.1-1.2016

3. Complete each statement.

   a. $235 \xrightarrow{+10}$ _____ $\xrightarrow{+100}$ _____

   b. $391 \xrightarrow{-100}$ _____ $\xrightarrow{-10}$ _____

   c. $417 \xrightarrow{-10}$ _____ $\xrightarrow{\quad}$ _____ $\xrightarrow{-100}$ 297

   d. $311 \xrightarrow{-10}$ _____ $\xrightarrow{-10}$ _____ $\xrightarrow{+100}$ _____ $\xrightarrow{+100}$ _____ $\xrightarrow{+10}$ _____

4. Solve using the arrow way.

   a. 370 + 110 = _____

   b. 290 + _____ = 400

   c. _____ + 710 = 850

Lesson 1: Relate 10 more, 10 less, 100 more, and 100 less to addition and subtraction of 10 and 100.

EUREKA MATH

©2015 Great Minds. eureka-math.org
G2-M5-SE-B3-1.3.1-1.2016

ones	tens	hundreds

hundreds place value chart

Lesson 1:   Relate 10 more, 10 less, 100 more, and 100 less to addition and subtraction of 10 and 100.

©2015 Great Minds. eureka-math.org
G2-M5-SE-B3-1.3.1-1.2016

This page intentionally left blank

unlabeled hundreds place value chart

Lesson 1:   Relate 10 more, 10 less, 100 more, and 100 less to addition and
            subtraction of 10 and 100.

7

©2015 Great Minds. eureka-math.org
G2-M5-SE-B3-1.3.1-1.2016

This page intentionally left blank

Name _____   Date _____

1. Solve each addition problem using place value strategies. Use the arrow way or mental math, and record your answers. You may use scrap paper if you like.

    a. 2 hundreds 4 tens + 3 hundreds = _____ hundreds _____ tens

       240 + 300 = _____

    b. 340 + 300 = _____   140 + 500 = _____   200 + 440 = _____

    c. 400 + 374 = _____   274 + 500 = _____   700 + 236 = _____

    d. 571 + _____ = 871   _____ + 349 = 749   96 + _____ = 696

    e. _____ + 562 = 862   300 + _____ = 783   600 + _____ = 726

2. Solve each subtraction problem using place value strategies. Use the arrow way or mental math, and record your answers. You may use scrap paper if you like.

    a. 6 hundreds 2 ones – 4 hundreds = _____ hundreds _____ tens _____ ones

       602 – 400 = _____

    b. 640 – 200 = _____   650 – 300 = _____   750 – _____ = 350

    c. 462 – 200 = _____   667 – 500 = _____   731 – 400 = _____

    d. 431 – _____ = 131   985 – _____ = 585   768 – _____ = 68

    e. _____ – 200 = 662   _____ – 300 = 653   734 – _____ =234

©2015 Great Minds. eureka-math.org
G2-M5-SE-B3-1.3.1-1.2016

3. Fill in the blanks to make true number sentences. Use place value strategies, number bonds, or the arrow way to solve.

   a. 200 more than 389 is _____.

   b. 300 more than _____ is 568.

   c. 400 less than 867 is _____.

   d. _____ less than 962 is 262.

4. Jessica's lemon tree had 526 lemons. She gave away 300 lemons. How many does she have left? Use the arrow way to solve.

Lesson 2:   Add and subtract multiples of 100, including counting on to subtract.

EUREKA MATH™

©2015 Great Minds. eureka-math.org
G2-M5-SE-B3-1.3.1-1.2016

Name _____ Date _____

1. Solve each addition problem using place value strategies. Use the arrow way or mental math, and record your answers. You may use scrap paper if you like.

   a. 4 hundreds 5 tens + 2 hundreds = _____ hundreds _____ tens

      450 + 200 = _____

   b. 220 + 300 = _____   230 + 500 = _____   200 + 440 = _____

   c. 400 + 368 = _____   386 + 500 = _____   700 + 239 = _____

   d. 119 + _____ = 519   _____ + 272 = 872   62 + _____ = 562

2. Solve each subtraction problem using place value strategies. Use the arrow way or mental math, and record your answers. You may use scrap paper if you like.

   a. 5 hundreds 8 ones – 3 hundreds = _____ hundreds _____ tens _____ ones

      508 – 300 = _____

   b. 430 – 200 = _____   550 – 300 = _____   860 – _____ = 360

   c. 628 – 200 = _____   718 – 500 = _____   836 – 400 = _____

   d. 553 – _____ = 153   981 – _____ = 381   827 – _____ = 27

EUREKA MATH™

Lesson 2:   Add and subtract multiples of 100, including counting on to subtract.

11

©2015 Great Minds. eureka-math.org
G2-M5-SE-B3-1.3.1-1.2016

3. Fill in the blanks to make true number sentences. Use place value strategies, number bonds, or the arrow way to solve.

   a. 300 more than 215 is _____.

   b. 300 more than _____ is 668.

   c. 500 less than 980 is _____.

   d. _____ less than 987 is 487.

   e. 600 _____ than 871 is 271.

   f. 400 _____ than 444 is 844.

EUREKA
MATH™

©2015 Great Minds. eureka-math.org
G2-M5-SE-B3-1.3.1-1.2016

Name _____   Date _____

1. Solve each set of problems using the arrow way.

a.
380 + 200
380 + 220
380 + 230

b.
470 + 400
470 + 430
470 + 450

c.
650 + 200
650 + 250
650 + 280

d.
430 + 300
430 + 370
430 + 390

©2015 Great Minds. eureka-math.org
G2-M5-SE-B3-1.3.1-1.2016

2. Solve using the arrow way or mental math. Use scrap paper if needed.

a. 490 + 200 = _____	210 + 490 = _____	490 + 220 = _____
b. 230 + 700 = _____	230 + 710 = _____	730 + 230 = _____
c. 260 + 240 = _____	260 + 260 = _____	280 + 260 = _____
d. 160 + 150 = _____	370 + 280 = _____	380 + 450 = _____
e. 430 + 290 = _____	660 + 180 = _____	370 + 270 = _____

3. Solve.

a. 66 tens + 20 tens = _____ tens   b. 66 tens + 24 tens = _____ tens

c. 66 tens + 27 tens = _____ tens   d. 67 tens + 28 tens = _____ tens

e. What is the value of 86 tens? _____

EUREKA
MATH

©2015 Great Minds. eureka-math.org
G2-M5-SE-B3-1.3.1-1.2016

Name _____   Date _____

1. Solve each set of problems using the arrow way.

a.	260 + 200
	260 + 240
	260 + 250
b.	320 + 400
	320 + 480
	320 + 490
c.	550 + 200
	550 + 250
	550 + 270
d.	230 + 400
	230 + 470
	230 + 490

©2015 Great Minds. eureka-math.org
G2-M5-SE-B3-1.3.1-1.2016

2. Solve using the arrow way or mental math. Use scrap paper if needed.

a. 320 + 200 = _____	280 + 320 = _____	290 + 320 = _____
b. 130 + 500 = _____	130 + 560 = _____	130 + 580 = _____
c. 360 + 240 = _____	350 + 270 = _____	380 + 230 = _____
d. 260 + 250 = _____	270 + 280 = _____	280 + 250 = _____
e. 440 + 280 = _____	660 + 160 = _____	770 + 150 = _____

3. Solve.

   a. 34 tens + 20 tens = _____ tens

   b. 34 tens + 26 tens = _____ tens

   c. 34 tens + 27 tens = _____ tens

   d. 34 tens + 28 tens = _____ tens

   e. What is the value of 62 tens? _____

Lesson 3:   Add multiples of 100 and some tens within 1,000.

EUREKA MATH

©2015 Great Minds. eureka-math.org
G2-M5-SE-B3-1.3.1-1.2016

Name _____ Date _____

1. Solve using the arrow way.

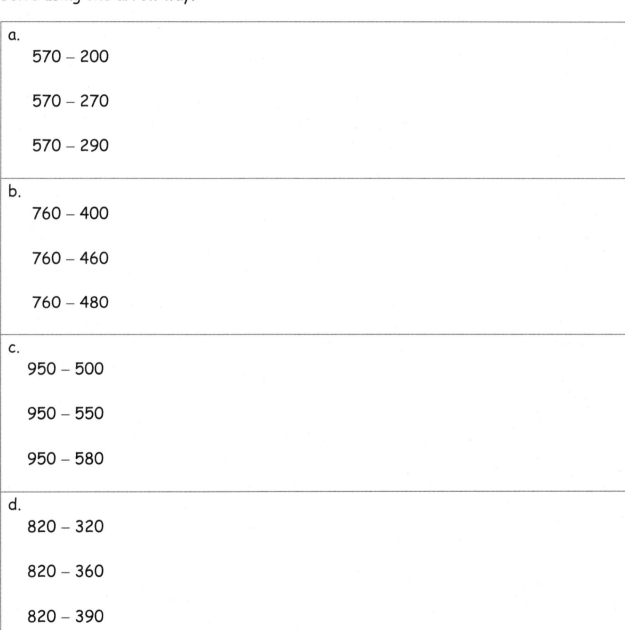

a.

570 – 200

570 – 270

570 – 290

b.

760 – 400

760 – 460

760 – 480

c.

950 – 500

950 – 550

950 – 580

d.

820 – 320

820 – 360

820 – 390

©2015 Great Minds. eureka-math.org
G2-M5-SE-B3-1.3.1-1.2016

2. Solve using the arrow way or mental math. Use scrap paper if needed.

a.

530 – 400 = _____   530 – 430 = _____   530 – 460 = _____

b.

950 – 550 = _____   950 – 660 = _____   950 – 680 = _____

c.

640 – 240 = _____   640 – 250 = _____   640 – 290 = _____

d.

740 – 440 = _____   740 – 650 = _____   740 – 690 = _____

3. Solve.

a. 88 tens – 20 tens = _____   b. 88 tens – 28 tens = _____

c. 88 tens – 29 tens = _____   d. 84 tens – 28 tens = _____

e. What is the value of 60 tens? _____

f. What is the value of 56 tens? _____

18   Lesson 4:   Subtract multiples of 100 and some tens within 1,000.

EUREKA
MATH

©2015 Great Minds. eureka-math.org
G2-M5-SE-B3-1.3.1-1.2016

Name _____   Date _____

1. Solve using the arrow way.

a.
430 – 200
430 – 230
430 – 240

b.
570 – 300
570 – 370
570 – 390

c.
750 – 400
750 – 450
750 – 480

d.
940 – 330
940 – 360
940 – 480

Lesson 4:   Subtract multiples of 100 and some tens within 1,000.

19

©2015 Great Minds. eureka-math.org
G2-M5-SE-B3-1.3.1-1.2016

2. Solve using the arrow way or mental math. Use scrap paper if needed.

a.	330 – 200 = _____	330 – 230 = _____	330 – 260 = _____
b.	440 – 240 = _____	440 – 260 = _____	440 – 290 = _____
c.	860 – 560 = _____	860 – 570 = _____	860 – 590 = _____
d.	970 – 470 = _____	970 – 480 = _____	970 – 490 = _____

3. Solve.

   a. 66 tens – 30 tens = _____   b. 66 tens – 36 tens = _____

   c. 66 tens – 38 tens = _____   d. 67 tens – 39 tens = _____

   e. What is the value of 28 tens? _____

   f. What is the value of 36 tens? _____

Lesson 4:   Subtract multiples of 100 and some tens within 1,000.

EUREKA
MATH™

©2015 Great Minds. eureka-math.org
G2-M5-SE-B3-1.3.1-1.2016

Name _____   Date _____

1. Solve.

   a. 30 tens = _____   b. 43 tens = _____

   c. 18 tens + 12 tens = _____ tens   d. 18 tens + 13 tens = _____ tens

   e. 24 tens + 19 tens = _____ tens   f. 25 tens + 29 tens = _____ tens

2. Add by drawing a number bond to make a hundred. Write the simplified equation and solve.

   a. 190 + 130

         10   120

   ____200 + 120____ = _____

   b. 260 + 190

   _____ = _____

   c. 330 + 180

   _____ = _____

EUREKA
MATH

Lesson 5:   Use the associative property to make a hundred in one addend.

21

©2015 Great Minds. eureka-math.org
G2-M5-SE-B3-1.3.1-1.2016

d. $440 + 280$

_____ = _____

e. $199 + 86$

_____ = _____

f. $298 + 57$

_____ = _____

g. $425 + 397$

_____ = _____

Lesson 5:   Use the associative property to make a hundred in one addend.

EUREKA MATH

©2015 Great Minds. eureka-math.org
G2-M5-SE-B3-1.3.1-1.2016

Name _____   Date _____

1. Solve.

    a. 32 tens = _____   b. 52 tens = _____

    c. 19 tens + 11 tens = _____ tens   d. 19 tens + 13 tens = _____ tens

    e. 28 tens + 23 tens = _____ tens   f. 28 tens + 24 tens = _____ tens

2. Add by drawing a number bond to make a hundred. Write the simplified equation and solve.

    a. 90 + 180

        $\wedge$

        10   170

        _____100 + 170_____ = _____

    b. 190 + 460

        _____ = _____

©2015 Great Minds. eureka-math.org
G2-M5-SE-B3-1.3.1-1.2016

c. 540 + 280

_____ = _____

d. 380 + 430

_____ = _____

e. 99 + 141

_____ = _____

f. 75 + 299

_____ = _____

g. 795 + 156

_____ = _____

Lesson 5:   Use the associative property to make a hundred in one addend.

EUREKA
MATH™

©2015 Great Minds. eureka-math.org
G2-M5-SE-B3-1.3.1-1.2016

Name _____ Date _____

1. Draw and label a tape diagram to show how to simplify the problem. Write the new equation , and then subtract.

a. 220 – 190 = __230 – 200__ = _____

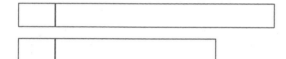

b. 320 – 190 = _____ = _____

c. 400 – 280 = _____ = _____

d. 470 – 280 = _____ = _____

e. 530 – 270 = _____ = _____

EUREKA MATH™ Lesson 6: Use the associative property to subtract from three-digit numbers and verify solutions with addition. 25

©2015 Great Minds. eureka-math.org
G2-M5-SE-B3-1.3.1-1.2016

2. Draw and label a tape diagram to show how to simplify the problem. Write a new equation, and then subtract. Check your work using addition.

a. 451 – 199 = ____452 – 200____ = _____

	Check:
+1 │   451   │
+1 │ 199 │	

b. 562 – 299 = _____ = _____

	Check:

c. 432 – 298 = _____ = _____

	Check:

d. 612 – 295 = _____ = _____

	Check:

Lesson 6:   Use the associative property to subtract from three-digit numbers and verify solutions with addition.

EUREKA MATH

©2015 Great Minds. eureka-math.org
G2-M5-SE-B3-1.3.1-1.2016

Name _____   Date _____

1. Draw and label a tape diagram to show how to simplify the problem. Write the new equation, and then subtract.

   a. 340 – 190 = ___350 – 200___ = _____

+ 10	340

+ 10	190

   b. 420 – 190 = _____ = _____

   c. 500 – 280 = _____ = _____

   d. 650 – 280 = _____ = _____

   e. 740 – 270 = _____ = _____

Lesson 6:   Use the associative property to subtract from three-digit numbers and verify solutions with addition.

27

©2015 Great Minds. eureka-math.org
G2-M5-SE-B3-1.3.1-1.2016

2. Draw and label a tape diagram to show how to simplify the problem. Write a new equation, and then subtract. Check your work using addition.

a. 236 – 99 = ____237 – 100____ = _____

	Check:
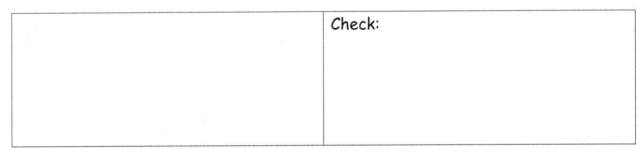	

b. 372 – 199 = _____ = _____

	Check:

c. 442 – 298 = _____ = _____

	Check:

d. 718 – 390 = _____ = _____

	Check:
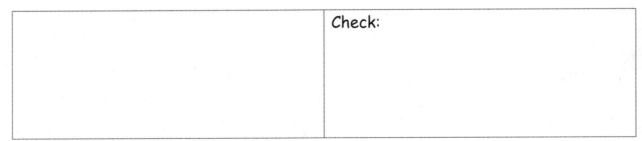	

Lesson 6:   Use the associative property to subtract from three-digit numbers and verify solutions with addition.

EUREKA
MATH™

©2015 Great Minds. eureka-math.org
G2-M5-SE-B3-1.3.1-1.2016

Name _____   Date _____

1. Circle the student work that shows a *correct* solution to 543 + 290.

	Explain the mistake in any of the incorrect solutions.
$543 + 290 = 533 + 300 = 833$ $\wedge$ 533 10	
$543 + 290 = 553 + 300 = 853$ $\boxed{+10}\ \boxed{543}$ $\boxed{+10}\ \boxed{290}$	_____ _____ _____ _____
$543 \xrightarrow{+200} 743 \xrightarrow{+60} 803 \xrightarrow{+30} 833$	_____

2. Circle the student work that *correctly* shows a strategy to solve 721 – 490.

$721 - 490 = 711 - 500 = 211$
$711 \overset{\wedge}{} 10$

$\boxed{+10}\ \boxed{721}$
$\boxed{+10}\ \boxed{490}$

$731 - 500 = 231$

Fix the work that is *incorrect* by making a new drawing in the space below with a matching number sentence.

©2015 Great Minds. eureka-math.org
G2-M5-SE-B3-1.3.1-1.2016

3. Two students solved 636 + 294 using two different strategies.

$636 \xrightarrow{+4} 640 \xrightarrow{+60} 700 \xrightarrow{+30} 730 \xrightarrow{+200} 930$

$$636 + 294 = 630 + 300 = 930$$

$$630 \quad 6$$

Explain which strategy would be easier to use when solving and why.

_____

_____

_____

4. Circle one of the strategies below, and use the circled strategy to solve 290 + 374.

a. *arrow way / number bond*	b. Solve:

c. Explain why you chose that strategy.

_____

_____

_____

Lesson 7:   Share and critique solution strategies for varied addition and subtraction problems within 1,000

©2015 Great Minds. eureka-math.org
G2-M5-SE-B3-1.3.1-1.2016

Name _____ Date _____

1. Solve each problem with a written strategy such as a tape diagram, a number bond, the arrow way, the vertical form, or chips on a place value chart.

a. 370 + 300 = _____	b. _____ = 562 – 200	c. _____ + 500 = 812
d. 230 - 190 = _____	e. _____= 640 – 180	f. 450 - 290 = _____

2. Use the arrow way to complete the number sentences.

a. 420 - 230 = _____	b. 340 - 160 = _____	c. 710 – 350 = _____

©2015 Great Minds. eureka-math.org
G2-M5-SE-B3-1.3.1-1.2016

3. Solve 667 + 295 using two different strategies.

a.	b.

c. Explain which strategy is easier to use when solving and why.

_____

_____

_____

4. Circle one of the strategies below, and use the circled strategy to solve 199 + 478.

a.	b. Solve:
arrow way / number bond	

c. Explain why you chose that strategy.

_____

_____

_____

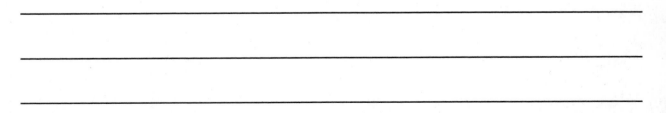

Lesson 7:   Share and critique solution strategies for varied addition and
subtraction problems within 1,000

EUREKA
MATH™

©2015 Great Minds. eureka-math.org
G2-M5-SE-B3-1.3.1-1.2016

Student A	Student B

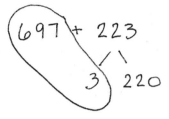

697 + 223

          / \
         3   220

700 + 220 = 920

697 $\xrightarrow{+3}$ 700 $\xrightarrow{+200}$ 900 $\xrightarrow{+20}$ 920

Student C	Student D

864 − 380
      / \
   844   20

844 − 400 = 444

+20 | 864

+20 | 380

884 − 400 = 484

student work samples

Lesson 7:   Share and critique solution strategies for varied addition and
subtraction problems within 1,000

33

©2015 Great Minds. eureka-math.org
G2-M5-SE-B3-1.3.1-1.2016

This page intentionally left blank

Name _____ Date _____

1. Solve the following problems using your place value chart, place value disks, and vertical form. Bundle a ten or hundred, when necessary.

a. 301 + 49	b. 402 + 48
c. 315 + 93	d. 216 + 192
e. 545 + 346	f. 565 + 226
g. 222 + 687	h. 164 + 745

©2015 Great Minds. eureka-math.org
G2-M5-SE-B3-1.3.1-1.2016

2. Solve.

   a.   300 + 200 = _____

   b.   320 + 200 = _____

   c.   320 + 230 = _____

   d.   320 + 280 = _____

   e.   328 + 286 = _____

   f.   600 + 80 = _____

   g.   600 + 180 = _____

   h.   620 + 180 = _____

   i.   680 + 220 = _____

   j.   680 + 230 = _____

Lesson 8:   Relate manipulative representations to the addition algorithm.

EUREKA
MATH™

©2015 Great Minds. eureka-math.org
G2-M5-SE-B3-1.3.1-1.2016

Name _____   Date _____

1. Solve the following problems using your place value chart, place value disks, and vertical form. Bundle a ten or hundred, when necessary.

a. 505 + 75	b. 606 + 84
c. 293 + 114	d. 314 + 495
e. 364 + 326	f. 346 + 234
g. 384 + 225	h. 609 + 351

©2015 Great Minds. eureka-math.org
G2-M5-SE-B3-1.3.1-1.2016

2. Solve.

   a. 200 + 400 = _____

   b. 220 + 400 = _____

   c. 220 + 440 = _____

   d. 220 + 480 = _____

   e. 225 + 485 = _____

   f. 500 + 60 = _____

   g. 500 + 160 = _____

   h. 540 + 160 = _____

   i. 560 + 240 = _____

   j. 560 + 250 = _____

Lesson 8:   Relate manipulative representations to the addition algorithm.

EUREKA
MATH

©2015 Great Minds. eureka-math.org
G2-M5-SE-B3-1.3.1-1.2016

Name _____   Date _____

1. Solve the following problems using place value disks, a place value chart, and vertical form.

a. 417 + 293	b. 526 + 185
c. 338 + 273	d. 625 + 186
e. 250 + 530	f. 243 + 537
g. 376 + 624	h. 283 + 657

©2015 Great Minds. eureka-math.org
G2-M5-SE-B3-1.3.1-1.2016

2. Solve.

   a. 270 + 430 = _____

   b. 260 + 440 = _____

   c. 255 + 445 = _____

   d. 258 + 443 = _____

   e. 408 + 303 = _____

   f. 478 + 303 = _____

   g. 478 + 323 = _____

Lesson 9:   Relate manipulative representations to the addition algorithm.

EUREKA
MATH™

©2015 Great Minds. eureka-math.org
G2-M5-SE-B3-1.3.1-1.2016

Name _____   Date _____

1. Solve the following problems using a place value chart, place value disks, and vertical form. Bundle a ten or hundred, when necessary.

a. 205 + 345	b. 365 + 406
c. 446 + 334	d. 466 + 226
e. 537 + 243	f. 358 + 443
g. 753 + 157	h. 663 + 258

©2015 Great Minds. eureka-math.org
G2-M5-SE-B3-1.3.1-1.2016

2. Solve.

   a. 180 + 420 = _____

   b. 190 + 430 = _____

   c. 364 + 236 = _____

   d. 275 + 435 = _____

   e. 404 + 206 = _____

   f. 440 + 260 = _____

   g. 444 + 266 = _____

Lesson 9:   Relate manipulative representations to the addition algorithm.

EUREKA
MATH™

©2015 Great Minds. eureka-math.org
G2-M5-SE-B3-1.3.1-1.2016

Name _____   Date _____

1. Solve using vertical form, and draw chips on the place value chart. Bundle as needed.

hundreds	tens	ones

a. 117 + 170 = _____

hundreds	tens	ones

b. 217 + 173 = _____

hundreds	tens	ones

c. 371 + 133 = _____

EUREKA MATH

Lesson 10:   Use math drawings to represent additions with up to two compositions and relate drawings to the addition algorithm.

43

©2015 Great Minds. eureka-math.org
G2-M5-SE-B3-1.3.1-1.2016

hundreds	tens	ones

d. 504 + 269 = _____

2. Solve using vertical form, and draw chips on a place value chart. Bundle as needed.

   a. 546 + 192 = _____

   b. 546 + 275 = _____

Lesson 10:   Use math drawings to represent additions with up to two
compositions and relate drawings to the addition algorithm.

EUREKA
MATH™

©2015 Great Minds. eureka-math.org
G2-M5-SE-B3-1.3.1-1.2016

Name _____   Date _____

1. Solve using vertical form, and draw chips on the place value chart. Bundle as needed.

hundreds	tens	ones

a. 124 + 260 = _____

hundreds	tens	ones

b. 426 + 324 = _____

hundreds	tens	ones

c. 362 + 243 = _____

©2015 Great Minds. eureka-math.org
G2-M5-SE-B3-1.3.1-1.2016

hundreds	tens	ones

d. 606 + 294 = _____

2. Solve using vertical form, and draw chips on a place value chart. Bundle as needed.

a. 372 + 118 = _____

b. 248 + 233 = _____

Lesson 10:   Use math drawings to represent additions with up to two
compositions and relate drawings to the addition algorithm.

©2015 Great Minds. eureka-math.org
G2-M5-SE-B3-1.3.1-1.2016

Name _____   Date _____

1. Solve using vertical form, and draw chips on the place value chart. Bundle as needed.

hundreds	tens	ones

a. 227 + 183 = _____

hundreds	tens	ones

b. 424 + 288 = _____

hundreds	tens	ones

c. 638 + 298 = _____

©2015 Great Minds. eureka-math.org
G2-M5-SE-B3-1.3.1-1.2016

hundreds	tens	ones

d. 648 + 289 = _____

2. Solve using vertical form, and draw chips on a place value chart. Bundle as needed.

a. 307 + 187

b. 398 + 207

Lesson 11:   Use math drawings to represent additions with up to two
compositions and relate drawings to the addition algorithm.

EUREKA
MATH™

©2015 Great Minds. eureka-math.org
G2-M5-SE-B3-1.3.1-1.2016

Name _____   Date _____

1. Solve using vertical form, and draw chips on the place value chart. Bundle as needed.

hundreds	tens	ones

a. 167 + 224 = _____

hundreds	tens	ones

b. 518 + 245 = _____

hundreds	tens	ones

c. 482 + 369 = _____

EUREKA MATH

Lesson 11:   Use math drawings to represent additions with up to two compositions and relate drawings to the addition algorithm.

49

©2015 Great Minds. eureka-math.org
G2-M5-SE-B3-1.3.1-1.2016

hundreds	tens	ones

d. 638 + 298 = _____

2. Solve using vertical form, and draw chips on a place value chart. Bundle as needed.

a. 456 + 378

b. 187 + 567

Lesson 11: Use math drawings to represent additions with up to two
compositions and relate drawings to the addition algorithm.

EUREKA MATH

©2015 Great Minds. eureka-math.org
G2-M5-SE-B3-1.3.1-1.2016

Name _____   Date _____

1. Tracy solved the problem 299 + 399 four different ways.

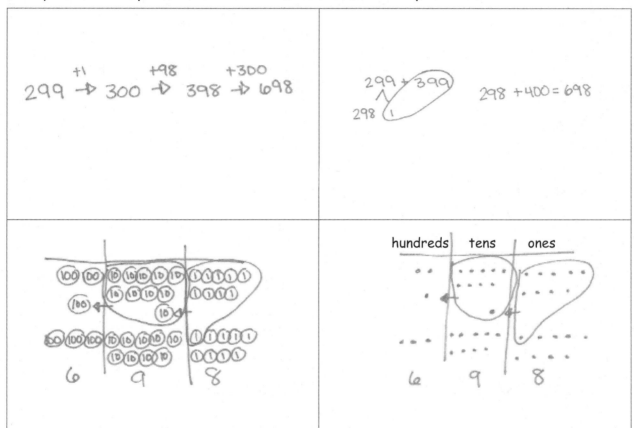

Explain which strategy is most efficient for Tracy to use and why.

_____

_____

_____

_____

_____

EUREKA MATH

Lesson 12:   Choose and explain solution strategies and record with a written addition method.

51

©2015 Great Minds. eureka-math.org
G2-M5-SE-B3-1.3.1-1.2016

2. Choose the best strategy and solve. Explain why you chose that strategy.

a. 221 + 498	Explanation: _____ _____ _____ _____
b. 467 + 200	Explanation: _____ _____ _____ _____
c. 378 + 464	Explanation: _____ _____ _____ _____

EUREKA MATH

©2015 Great Minds. eureka-math.org
G2-M5-SE-B3-1.3.1-1.2016

Name _____   Date _____

1. Solve 435 + 290 using two different strategies.

a.	b.

c. Explain which strategy would be easier and why.

_____

_____

_____

_____

Lesson 12:   Choose and explain solution strategies and record with a written addition method.

53

©2015 Great Minds. eureka-math.org
G2-M5-SE-B3-1.3.1-1.2016

2. Choose the best strategy and solve. Explain why you chose that strategy.

a. 299 + 458	Explanation: _____ _____ _____ _____
b. 733 + 210	Explanation: _____ _____ _____ _____
c. 295 + 466	Explanation: _____ _____ _____ _____

Lesson 12: Choose and explain solution strategies and record with a written addition method.

EUREKA MATH™

©2015 Great Minds. eureka-math.org
G2-M5-SE-B3-1.3.1-1.2016

Name _____   Date _____

1. Solve using mental math.

   a. 8 – 6 = _____   80 – 60 = _____   180 – 60 = _____   180 – 59 = _____

   b. 6 – 3 = _____   60 – 30 = _____   760 – 30 = _____   760 – 28 = _____

2. Solve using mental math or vertical form with place value disks. Check your work using addition.

   a. 138 – 17 = ___121___   b. 138 – 19 = _____

   ```
   138        121
   –17       + 17
   121        138
   ```

   c. 445 – 35 = _____   d. 445 – 53 = _____

EUREKA
MATH™

Lesson 13:   Relate manipulative representations to the subtraction algorithm, and
              use addition to explain why the subtraction method works.

55

©2015 Great Minds. eureka-math.org
G2-M5-SE-B3-1.3.1-1.2016

e. 863 – 170 = _____

f. 845 – 152 = _____

g. 472 – 228 = _____

h. 418 – 274 = _____

i. 567 – 184 = _____

j. 567 – 148 = _____

Lesson 13:   Relate manipulative representations to the subtraction algorithm, and use addition to explain why the subtraction method works.

EUREKA MATH™

©2015 Great Minds. eureka-math.org
G2-M5-SE-B3-1.3.1-1.2016

Name _____   Date _____

1. Solve using mental math.

   a. 9 – 5 = _____   90 – 50 = _____   190 – 50 = _____   190 – 49 = _____

   b. 7 – 4 = _____   70 – 40 = _____   370 – 40 = _____   370 – 39 = _____

2. Solve using mental math or vertical form with place value disks. Check your work using addition.

   a. 153 – 31 = ___122___   b. 153 – 38 = _____

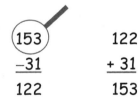

   c. 362 – 49 = _____   d. 485 – 177 = _____

©2015 Great Minds. eureka-math.org
G2-M5-SE-B3-1.3.1-1.2016

e. 753 – 290 = _____

f. 567 – 290 = _____

g. 873 – 428 = _____

h. 817 – 565 = _____

i. 973 – 681 = _____

j. 748 – 239 = _____

3. Complete the number sentence modeled by place value disks.

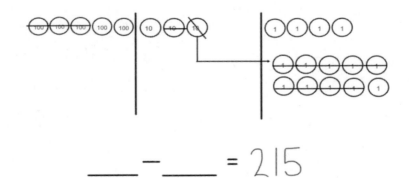

_____ – _____ = 215

Lesson 13: Relate manipulative representations to the subtraction algorithm, and use addition to explain why the subtraction method works.

EUREKA
MATH™

©2015 Great Minds. eureka-math.org
G2-M5-SE-B3-1.3.1-1.2016

Name _____   Date _____

1. Solve by drawing place value disks on a chart. Then, use addition to check your work.

a. 469 – 170	Solve vertically or mentally:	Check:
b. 531 – 224	Solve vertically or mentally:	Check:
c. 618 – 229	Solve vertically or mentally:	Check:

Use math drawings to represent subtraction with up to two decompositions, relate drawings to the algorithm, and use addition to explain why the subtraction method works.

©2015 Great Minds. eureka-math.org
G2-M5-SE-B3-1.3.1-1.2016

d. 838 – 384	Solve vertically or mentally:	Check:
e. 927 – 628	Solve vertically or mentally:	Check:

2. If 561 – 387 = 174, then 174 + 387 = 561. Explain why this statement is true using numbers, pictures, or words.

Lesson 14:   Use math drawings to represent subtraction with up to two decompositions, relate drawings to the algorithm, and use addition to explain why the subtraction method works.

©2015 Great Minds. eureka-math.org
G2-M5-SE-B3-1.3.1-1.2016

EUREKA
MATH™

Name _____   Date _____

1. Solve by drawing place value disks on a chart. Then, use addition to check your work.

a. 373 – 180	Solve vertically or mentally:	Check:
b. 463 – 357	Solve vertically or mentally:	Check:
c. 723 – 584	Solve vertically or mentally:	Check:

Lesson 14:   Use math drawings to represent subtraction with up to two decompositions, relate drawings to the algorithm, and use addition to explain why the subtraction method works.

61

©2015 Great Minds. eureka-math.org
G2-M5-SE-B3-1.3.1-1.2016

d. 861 – 673	Solve vertically or mentally:	Check:
e. 898 – 889	Solve vertically or mentally:	Check:

2. If 544 + 366 = 910, then 910 – 544 = 366. Explain why this statement is true using numbers, pictures, or words.

Lesson 14:   Use math drawings to represent subtraction with up to two decompositions, relate drawings to the algorithm, and use addition to explain why the subtraction method works.

EUREKA MATH

©2015 Great Minds. eureka-math.org
G2-M5-SE-B3-1.3.1-1.2016

Name _____   Date _____

1. Solve by drawing chips on the place value chart. Then, use addition to check your work.

a. 699 – 210 hundreds | tens | ones	Solve vertically or mentally:	Check:
b. 758 – 387 hundreds | tens | ones	Solve vertically or mentally:	Check:
c. 788 – 299 hundreds | tens | ones	Solve vertically or mentally:	Check:

   Lesson 15:   Use math drawings to represent subtraction with up to two   63
                                decompositions, relate drawings to the algorithm, and use addition to
                                explain why the subtraction method works.

©2015 Great Minds. eureka-math.org
G2-M5-SE-B3-1.3.1-1.2016

d. 821 – 523 hundreds tens ones	Solve vertically or mentally:	Check:
e. 913 – 558 hundreds tens ones	Solve vertically or mentally:	Check:

2. Complete all of the *if...then* statements. Draw a number bond to represent the related facts.

   a. If **762 – _____ = 173**, then **173 + 589 = _____.**

   b. If **631 – _____ = 273**, then **_____ + 273 = 631.**

   Use math drawings to represent subtraction with up to two decompositions, relate drawings to the algorithm, and use addition to explain why the subtraction method works.

EUREKA MATH™

©2015 Great Minds. eureka-math.org
G2-M5-SE-B3-1.3.1-1.2016

Name _____   Date _____

1. Solve by drawing chips on the place value chart. Then, use addition to check your work.

a. 800 – 675 hundreds │ tens │ ones	Solve vertically or mentally:	Check:
b. 742 – 495 hundreds │ tens │ ones	Solve vertically or mentally:	Check:
c. 657 – 290 hundreds │ tens │ ones	Solve vertically or mentally:	Check:

Lesson 15: Use math drawings to represent subtraction with up to two decompositions, relate drawings to the algorithm, and use addition to explain why the subtraction method works.

65

©2015 Great Minds. eureka-math.org
G2-M5-SE-B3-1.3.1-1.2016

d. 877 – 398 hundreds | tens | ones	Solve vertically or mentally:	Check:
e. 941 – 628 hundreds | tens | ones	Solve vertically or mentally:	Check:

2. Complete all of the *if…then* statements. Draw a number bond to represent the related facts.

   a. If **928 – _____ = 519**, then **519 + 409 = _____.**

   b. If **764 – _____ = 391**, then _____ **+ 391 = 764.**

Lesson 15:   Use math drawings to represent subtraction with up to two decompositions, relate drawings to the algorithm, and use addition to explain why the subtraction method works.

EUREKA MATH

©2015 Great Minds. eureka-math.org
G2-M5-SE-B3-1.3.1-1.2016

Name _____   Date _____

1. Solve vertically or using mental math. Draw chips on the place value chart and unbundle, if needed.

   a. 304 – 53 = _____

hundreds	tens	ones

   b. 406 – 187 = _____

hundreds	tens	ones

   c. 501 – 316 = _____

hundreds	tens	ones

©2015 Great Minds. eureka-math.org
G2-M5-SE-B3-1.3.1-1.2016

d. 700 − 509 = _____

hundreds	tens	ones

e. 900 − 626 = _____

hundreds	tens	ones

2. Emily said that 400 − 247 is the same as 399 − 246. Write an explanation using pictures, numbers, or words to prove Emily is correct.

Lesson 16: Subtract from multiples of 100 and from numbers with zero in the tens place.

EUREKA MATH

©2015 Great Minds. eureka-math.org
G2-M5-SE-B3-1.3.1-1.2016

Name _____ Date _____

1. Solve vertically or using mental math. Draw chips on the place value chart and unbundle, if needed.

a. 206 – 89 = _____

hundreds	tens	ones

b. 509 – 371 = _____

hundreds	tens	ones

c. 607 – 288 = _____

hundreds	tens	ones

EUREKA MATH

Lesson 16:   Subtract from multiples of 100 and from numbers with zero in the tens place.

69

©2015 Great Minds. eureka-math.org
G2-M5-SE-B3-1.3.1-1.2016

d. 800 − 608 = _____

hundreds	tens	ones

e. 900 − 572 = _____

hundreds	tens	ones

2. Andy said that 599 − 456 is the same as 600 − 457. Write an explanation using pictures, numbers, or words to prove Andy is correct.

Lesson 16:   Subtract from multiples of 100 and from numbers with zero in the tens place.

EUREKA MATH™

©2015 Great Minds. eureka-math.org
G2-M5-SE-B3-1.3.1-1.2016

Name _____ Date _____

1. Solve vertically or using mental math. Draw chips on the place value chart and unbundle, if needed.

a. 200 – 113 = _____

hundreds	tens	ones

b. 400 – 247 = _____

hundreds	tens	ones

c. 700 – 428 = _____

hundreds	tens	ones

Lesson 17:   Subtract from multiples of 100 and from numbers with zero in the tens place.

71

©2015 Great Minds. eureka-math.org
G2-M5-SE-B3-1.3.1-1.2016

d. 800 – 606 = _____

hundreds	tens	ones

e. 901 – 404 = _____

hundreds	tens	ones

2. Solve 600 – 367. Then, check your work using addition.

Solution:	Check:

Lesson 17:   Subtract from multiples of 100 and from numbers with zero in the tens
                        place.

EUREKA
MATH™

©2015 Great Minds. eureka-math.org
G2-M5-SE-B3-1.3.1-1.2016

Name _____   Date _____

1. Solve vertically or using mental math. Draw chips on the place value chart and unbundle, if needed.

a. 200 – 123 = _____

hundreds	tens	ones

b. 400 – 219 = _____

hundreds	tens	ones

c. 700 – 542 = _____

hundreds	tens	ones

Lesson 17:   Subtract from multiples of 100 and from numbers with zero in the tens place.

73

©2015 Great Minds. eureka-math.org
G2-M5-SE-B3-1.3.1-1.2016

d. 800 – 409 = _____

hundreds	tens	ones

e. 905 – 606 = _____

hundreds	tens	ones

2. Solve 800 – 567. Then, check your work using addition.

Solution:	Check:

Lesson 17: Subtract from multiples of 100 and from numbers with zero in the tens place.

EUREKA
MATH

©2015 Great Minds. eureka-math.org
G2-M5-SE-B3-1.3.1-1.2016

Name _____   Date _____

1. Use the arrow way and counting on to solve.

a. 300 – 247	b. 600 – 465

2. Solve vertically, and draw a place value chart and chips. Rename in one step.

a. 507 – 359	b. 708 – 529

3. Choose a strategy to solve, and explain why you chose that strategy.

a. 600 – 437	Explanation:

©2015 Great Minds. eureka-math.org
G2-M5-SE-B3-1.3.1-1.2016

b. 808 – 597	Explanation:

4. Prove the student's strategy by solving both problems to check that their solutions are the same. Explain to your partner why this way works.

799 – 542
= 800 – 543
Now I don't have to change for smaller units!

$$800 \atop -543$$ $$799 \atop -542$$

5. Use the simplifying strategy from Problem 4 to solve the following two problems.

a. 600 – 547	b. 700 – 513

Lesson 18:   Apply and explain alternate methods for subtracting from multiples of 100 and from numbers with zero in the tens place.

EUREKA MATH™

©2015 Great Minds. eureka-math.org
G2-M5-SE-B3-1.3.1-1.2016

Name _____ Date _____

1. Use the arrow way and counting on to solve.

a. 700 – 462	b. 900 – 232

2. Solve vertically, and draw a place value chart and chips. Rename in one step.

a. 907 – 467	b. 803 – 667

3. Choose a strategy to solve, and explain why you chose that strategy.

a. 700 – 390	Explanation:

EUREKA MATH

Lesson 18: Apply and explain alternate methods for subtracting from multiples of 100 and from numbers with zero in the tens place.

77

©2015 Great Minds. eureka-math.org
G2-M5-SE-B3-1.3.1-1.2016

b. 919 – 657	Explanation:

4. Explain why 300 – 186 is the same as 299 – 185.

Explanation:

5. Solve 500 – 278 using the simplifying strategy from Problem 4.

Solution:

Lesson 18:   Apply and explain alternate methods for subtracting from multiples of 100 and from numbers with zero in the tens place.

EUREKA
MATH™

©2015 Great Minds. eureka-math.org
G2-M5-SE-B3-1.3.1-1.2016

Name _____   Date _____

1. Explain how the two strategies to solve 500 − 211 are related.

a.	b.
hundreds | tens | ones 2 8 9	 $\begin{array}{r} 4\,9\,10 \\ \cancel{500} \\ -211 \\ \hline 289 \end{array}$

_____

_____

_____

_____

_____

_____

EUREKA
MATH™

Lesson 19:   Choose and explain solution strategies and record with a written
addition or subtraction method.

79

©2015 Great Minds. eureka-math.org
G2-M5-SE-B3-1.3.1-1.2016

2. Solve and explain why you chose that strategy.

a. 220 + 390 = _____	Explanation: _____ _____ _____ _____
b. 547 – 350 = _____	Explanation: _____ _____ _____ _____
c. 464 + 146 = _____	Explanation: _____ _____ _____ _____
d. 600 – 389 = _____	Explanation: _____ _____ _____ _____

Lesson 19:   Choose and explain solution strategies and record with a written addition or subtraction method.

EUREKA MATH

©2015 Great Minds. eureka-math.org
G2-M5-SE-B3-1.3.1-1.2016

Name _____   Date _____

1. Solve and explain why you chose that strategy.

a. 340 + 250 = _____	Explanation: _____ _____ _____ _____
b. 490 + 350 = _____	Explanation: _____ _____ _____ _____
c. 519 + 342 = _____	Explanation: _____ _____ _____ _____

Lesson 19:   Choose and explain solution strategies and record with a written
                   addition or subtraction method.

81

©2015 Great Minds. eureka-math.org
G2-M5-SE-B3-1.3.1-1.2016

d. 610 + _____ = 784	Explanation: _____ _____ _____ _____
e. 700 – 456 = _____	Explanation: _____ _____ _____ _____
f. 904 – 395 = _____	Explanation: _____ _____ _____ _____

Lesson 19:   Choose and explain solution strategies and record with a written addition or subtraction method.   **EUREKA MATH**

©2015 Great Minds. eureka-math.org
G2-M5-SE-B3-1.3.1-1.2016

Name _____   Date _____

Step 1:   Show your strategy to solve.

Step 2:   Find a classmate who used a different strategy, and copy his work into the box.

Step 3:   Discuss which strategy is more efficient.

1. 399 + 237 = _____

a. My strategy	b. _____'s strategy

2. 400 – 298 = _____

a. My strategy	b. _____'s strategy

Lesson 20:   Choose and explain solution strategies and record with a written addition or subtraction method.

83

©2015 Great Minds. eureka-math.org
G2-M5-SE-B3-1.3.1-1.2016

3.   548 + 181 = _____

a. My strategy	b. _____'s strategy

4.   360 + _____ = 754

a. My strategy	b. _____'s strategy

5.   862 – _____ = 690

a. My strategy	b. _____'s strategy

Lesson 20:   Choose and explain solution strategies and record with a written
                             addition or subtraction method.

©2015 Great Minds. eureka-math.org
G2-M5-SE-B3-1.3.1-1.2016

Name _____ Date _____

Solve each problem using two different strategies.

1. 456 + 244 = _____

a. First Strategy	b. Second Strategy

2. 698 + _____ = 945

a. First Strategy	b. Second Strategy

EUREKA MATH™

Lesson 20: Choose and explain solution strategies and record with a written addition or subtraction method.

85

©2015 Great Minds. eureka-math.org
G2-M5-SE-B3-1.3.1-1.2016

Circle a strategy to solve, and explain why you chose that strategy.

3. 257 + 160 = _____

    a. *Arrow way or vertical form*

b. Solve:	c. Explanation:
	_____
	_____
	_____
	_____
	_____

4. 754 – 597 = _____

    a. *Number bond or arrow way*

b. Solve:	c. Explanation:
	_____
	_____
	_____
	_____
	_____

Lesson 20:   Choose and explain solution strategies and record with a written addition or subtraction method.

©2015 Great Minds. eureka-math.org
G2-M5-SE-B3-1.3.1-1.2016

Student Edition

Eureka Math
Grade 2
Module 6

Special thanks go to the Gordon A. Cain Center and to the Department of Mathematics at Louisiana State University for their support in the development of *Eureka Math*.

Published by the non-profit Great Minds

Copyright © 2015 Great Minds. No part of this work may be reproduced, sold, or commercialized, in whole or in part, without written permission from Great Minds. Non-commercial use is licensed pursuant to a Creative Commons Attribution-NonCommercial-ShareAlike 4.0 license; for more information, go to http://greatminds.net/maps/math/copyright. "Great Minds" and "Eureka Math" are registered trademarks of Great Minds.

Printed in the U.S.A.

This book may be purchased from the publisher at eureka-math.org

10 9 8 7 6 5 4 3 2

ISBN 978-1-63255-295-2

Name _____   Date _____

1. Circle groups of two apples.

There are _____ groups of two apples.

2. Circle groups of three balls.

There are _____ groups of three balls.

3. Redraw the 12 oranges into 4 equal groups.

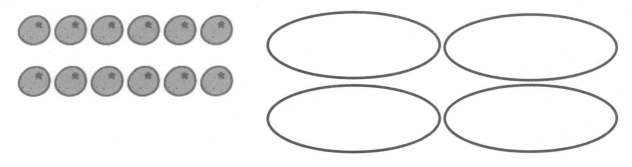

4 groups of _____ oranges

4. Redraw the 12 oranges into 3 equal groups.

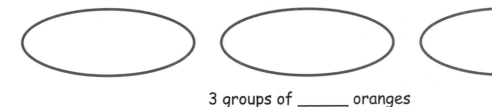

3 groups of _____ oranges

©2015 Great Minds. eureka-math.org
G2-M6-SE-B3-1.3.1-1.2016

5. Redraw the flowers to make each of the 3 groups have an equal number.

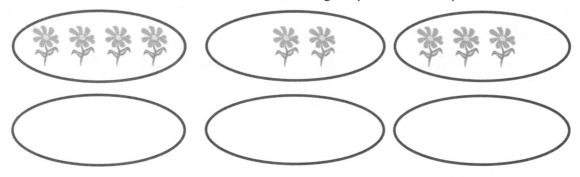

3 groups of _____ flowers = _____ flowers.

6. Redraw the lemons to make 2 equal size groups.

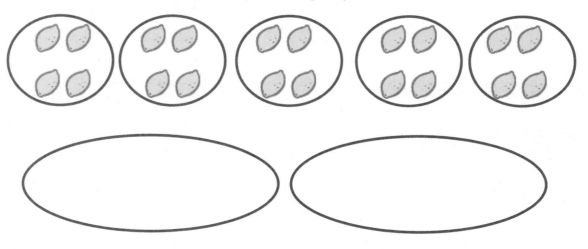

2 groups of _____ lemons = _____ lemons.

EUREKA
MATH™

©2015 Great Minds. eureka-math.org
G2-M6-SE-B3-1.3.1-1.2016

Name _____   Date _____

1. Circle groups of two shirts.

There are _____ groups of two shirts.

2. Circle groups of three pants.

There are _____ groups of three pants.

3. Redraw the 12 wheels into 3 equal groups.

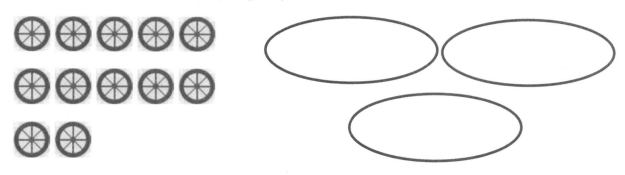

3 groups of _____ wheels

4. Redraw the 12 wheels into 4 equal groups.

4 groups of _____ wheels

©2015 Great Minds. eureka-math.org
G2-M6-SE-B3-1.3.1-1.2016

5. Redraw the apples to make each of the 4 groups have an equal amount.

4 groups of _____ apples = _____ apples.

6. Redraw the oranges to make 3 equal groups.

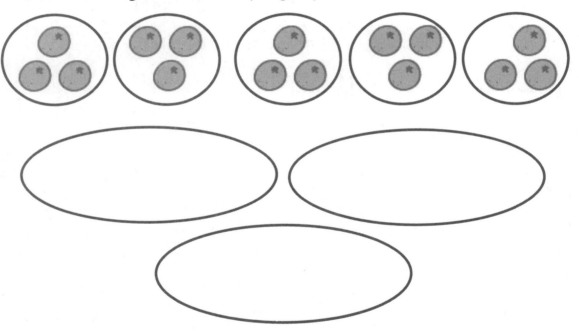

3 groups of _____ oranges = _____ oranges.

Lesson 1:   Use manipulatives to create equal groups.

EUREKA
MATH

©2015 Great Minds. eureka-math.org
G2-M6-SE-B3-1.3.1-1.2016

Name _____   Date _____

1. Write a repeated addition equation to show the number of objects in each group. Then, find the total.

a.
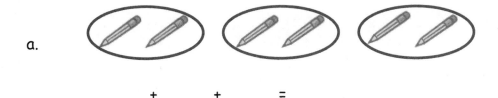

_____ + _____ + _____ = _____

3 groups of _____ = _____

b.
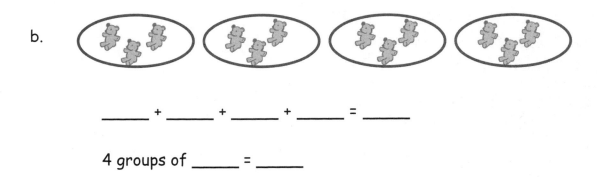

_____ + _____ + _____ + _____ = _____

4 groups of _____ = _____

2. Draw 1 more group of four. Then, write a repeated addition equation to match.

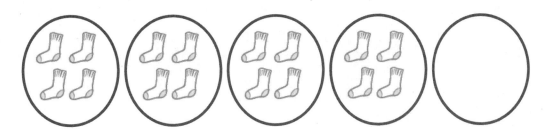

_____ + _____ + _____ + _____ + _____ = _____

5 groups of _____ = _____

Lesson 2:   Use math drawings to represent equal groups, and relate to repeated addition.

5

©2015 Great Minds. eureka-math.org
G2-M6-SE-B3-1.3.1-1.2016

3. Draw 1 more group of three. Then, write a repeated addition equation to match.

_____ + _____ + _____ + _____ = _____

_____ groups of 3 = _____

4. Draw 2 more equal groups. Then, write a repeated addition equation to match.

_____ + _____ + _____ + _____ + _____ = _____

_____ groups of 2 = _____

5. Draw 3 groups of 5 stars. Then, write a repeated addition equation to match.

Lesson 2:   Use math drawings to represent equal groups, and relate to repeated addition.

EUREKA MATH

©2015 Great Minds. eureka-math.org
G2-M6-SE-B3-1.3.1-1.2016

Name _____   Date _____

1. Write a repeated addition equation to show the number of objects in each group. Then, find the total.

a.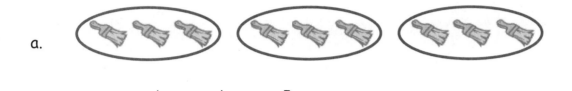

_____ + _____ + _____ = _____

3 groups of _____ = _____

b.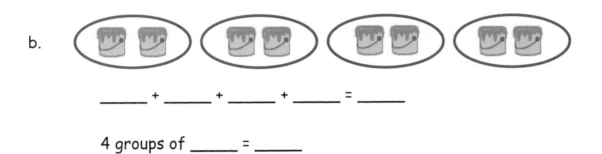

_____ + _____ + _____ + _____ = _____

4 groups of _____ = _____

2. Draw 1 more equal group.

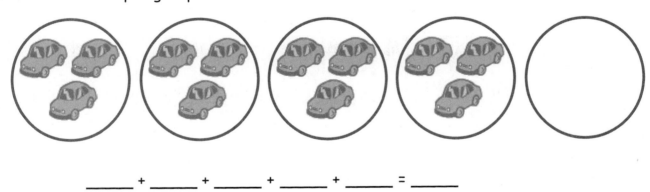

_____ + _____ + _____ + _____ + _____ = _____

5 groups of _____ = _____

EUREKA MATH

Lesson 2:   Use math drawings to represent equal groups, and relate to repeated addition.

7

©2015 Great Minds. eureka-math.org
G2-M6-SE-B3-1.3.1-1.2016

3. Draw 1 more group of four. Then, write a repeated addition equation to match.

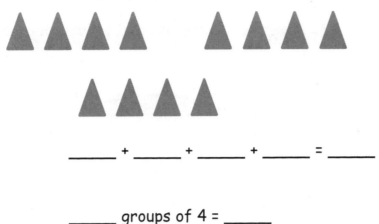

_____ + _____ + _____ + _____ = _____

_____ groups of 4 = _____

4. Draw 2 more equal groups. Then, write a repeated addition equation to match.

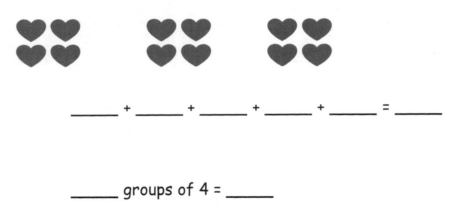

_____ + _____ + _____ + _____ + _____ = _____

_____ groups of 4 = _____

5. Draw 4 groups of 3 circles. Then, write a repeated addition equation to match.

Lesson 2: Use math drawings to represent equal groups, and relate to repeated addition.

EUREKA
MATH™

©2015 Great Minds. eureka-math.org
G2-M6-SE-B3-1.3.1-1.2016

Name _____   Date _____

1. Write a repeated addition equation to match the picture. Then, group the addends into pairs to show a more efficient way to add.

a.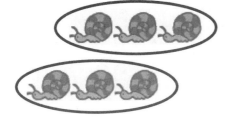

    _____ + _____ + _____ + _____ = _____

        \   /   \   /

    _____ + _____ = _____

    4 groups of _____ = 2 groups of _____

b.

    _____ + _____ + _____ + _____ = _____

        _____ + _____ = _____

    4 groups of _____ = 2 groups of _____

EUREKA MATH™

©2015 Great Minds. eureka-math.org
G2-M6-SE-B3-1.3.1-1.2016

c.

_____ + _____ + _____ + _____ + _____ + _____ + _____ + _____ = _____

_____ + _____ + _____ + _____ = _____

8 groups of _____ = 4 groups of _____

2. Write a repeated addition equation to match the picture. Then, group addends into pairs, and add to find the total.

a.

_____ + _____ + _____ + _____ + _____ = _____

_____ + _____ + 3 = _____

_____ + 3 = _____

b.

_____ + _____ + _____ = _____

_____ + 3 = _____

Lesson 3:   Use math drawings to represent equal groups, and relate to repeated addition.

EUREKA MATH

©2015 Great Minds. eureka-math.org
G2-M6-SE-B3-1.3.1-1.2016

Name _____   Date _____

1. Write a repeated addition equation to match the picture. Then, group the addends into pairs to show a more efficient way to add.

a.

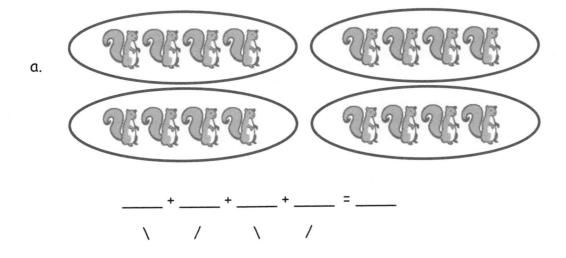

_____ + _____ + _____ + _____ = _____

\   /   \   /

_____   +   _____   =   _____

4 groups of _____ = 2 groups of _____

b.

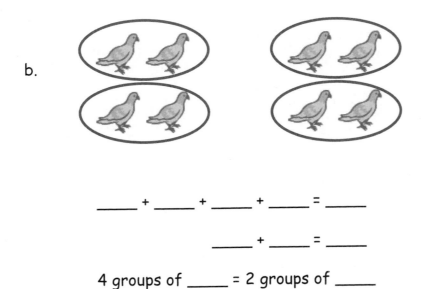

_____ + _____ + _____ + _____ = _____

_____ + _____ = _____

4 groups of _____ = 2 groups of _____

EUREKA MATH™

©2015 Great Minds. eureka-math.org
G2-M6-SE-B3-1.3.1-1.2016

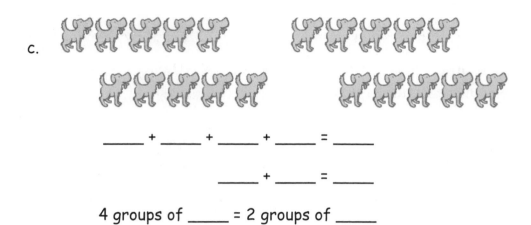

c.

_____ + _____ + _____ + _____ = _____

_____ + _____ = _____

4 groups of _____ = 2 groups of _____

2. Write a repeated addition equation to match the picture. Then, group addends into pairs, and add to find the total.

a.

_____ + _____ + _____ + _____ + _____ = _____

_____ + _____ + 3 = _____

_____ + 3 = _____

b.

_____ + _____ + _____ + _____ + _____ = _____

_____ + _____ + 2 = _____

_____ + 2 = _____

Lesson 3:   Use math drawings to represent equal groups, and relate to repeated addition.

EUREKA MATH

©2015 Great Minds. eureka-math.org
G2-M6-SE-B3-1.3.1-1.2016

Name _____   Date _____

1. Write a repeated addition equation to find the total of each tape diagram.

   a.

   _____ + _____ + _____ + _____ = _____

   4 groups of 2 = _____

   b.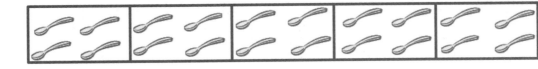

   _____ + _____ + _____ + _____ + _____ = _____

   5 groups of _____ = _____

   c. | 5 | 5 | 5 |
         |---|---|---|

   _____ + _____ + _____ = _____

   3 groups of _____ = _____

   d. | 3 | 3 | 3 | 3 | 3 | 3 |
         |---|---|---|---|---|---|

   _____ + _____ + _____ + _____ + _____ + _____ = _____

   _____ groups of _____ = _____

Lesson 4:   Represent equal groups with tape diagrams, and relate to repeated addition.

©2015 Great Minds. eureka-math.org
G2-M6-SE-B3-1.3.1-1.2016

2. Draw a tape diagram to find the total.

   a. 3 + 3 + 3 + 3 = _____

   b. 4 + 4 + 4 = _____

   c. 5 groups of 2

   d. 4 groups of 4

   e.

Lesson 4:   Represent equal groups with tape diagrams, and relate to repeated addition.

EUREKA MATH

©2015 Great Minds. eureka-math.org
G2-M6-SE-B3-1.3.1-1.2016

Name _____   Date _____

1. Write a repeated addition equation to find the total of each tape diagram.

a.

_____ + _____ + _____ + _____ = _____

4 groups of 3 = _____

b.

_____ + _____ + _____ + _____ + _____ = _____

5 groups of _____ = _____

c. | 4 | 4 | 4 | 4 |

_____ + _____ + _____ + _____ = _____

4 groups of _____ = _____

d. | 2 | 2 | 2 | 2 | 2 | 2 |

_____ + _____ + _____ + _____ + _____ + _____ = _____

_____ groups of _____ = _____

EUREKA MATH

Lesson 4:   Represent equal groups with tape diagrams, and relate to repeated addition.

15

©2015 Great Minds. eureka-math.org
G2-M6-SE-B3-1.3.1-1.2016

2. Draw a tape diagram to find the total.

a. 5 + 5 + 5 + 5 = _____

b. 4 + 4 + 4 + 4 + 4 = _____

c. 4 groups of 2

d. 5 groups of 3

e.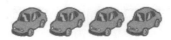

Lesson 4:   Represent equal groups with tape diagrams, and relate to repeated
                        addition.

                                                                    **EUREKA
                                                                    MATH**™

©2015 Great Minds. eureka-math.org
G2-M6-SE-B3-1.3.1-1.2016

Name _____   Date _____

1. Circle groups of four. Then, draw the triangles into 2 equal rows.

_____

_____

2. Circle groups of two. Redraw the groups of two as rows and then as columns.

3. Circle groups of three. Redraw the groups of three as rows and then as columns.

EUREKA
MATH™

Lesson 5:   Compose arrays from rows and columns, and count to find the total
             using objects.   17

©2015 Great Minds. eureka-math.org
G2-M6-SE-B3-1.3.1-1.2016

4. Count the objects in the arrays from left to right by rows and by columns. As you count, circle the rows and then the columns.

a.

b.

5. Redraw the circles and stars in Problem 4 as columns of two.

6. Draw an array with 15 triangles.

7. Show a different array with 15 triangles.

Lesson 5:   Compose arrays from rows and columns, and count to find the total using objects.

EUREKA MATH

©2015 Great Minds. eureka-math.org
G2-M6-SE-B3-1.3.1-1.2016

Name _____ Date _____

1. Circle groups of five. Then, draw the clouds into two equal rows.

_____

_____

2. Circle groups of four. Redraw the groups of four as rows and then as columns.

3. Circle groups of four. Redraw the groups of four as rows and then as columns.

EUREKA
MATH™

Lesson 5:   Compose arrays from rows and columns, and count to find the total using objects.

19

©2015 Great Minds. eureka-math.org
G2-M6-SE-B3-1.3.1-1.2016

4. Count the objects in the arrays from left to right by rows and by columns. As you count, circle the rows and then the columns.

a.

b.

5. Redraw the smiley faces and triangles in Problem 4 as columns of three.

6. Draw an array with 20 triangles.

7. Show a different array with 20 triangles.

Lesson 5:   Compose arrays from rows and columns, and count to find the total using objects.

EUREKA MATH™

©2015 Great Minds. eureka-math.org
G2-M6-SE-B3-1.3.1-1.2016

Name _____   Date _____

1. Complete each missing part describing each array.

Circle rows.   Circle columns.

a.   b.

    5 rows of _____ = _____   3 columns of _____ = _____

    ___ + ___ + ___ + ___ + ___ = ___   ____ + ____ + ____ = ____

Circle rows.   Circle columns.

c.   d.

    4 rows of _____ = _____   5 columns of _____ = _____

    ___ + ___ + ___ + ___ = ___   ___ + ___ + ___ + ___ + ___ = ___

©2015 Great Minds. eureka-math.org
G2-M6-SE-B3-1.3.1-1.2016

2. Use the array of triangles to answer the questions below.

   a. _____ rows of _____ = 12

   b. _____ columns of _____ = 12

   c. _____ + _____ + _____ = _____

   d. Add 1 more row. How many triangles are there now? _____

   e. Add 1 more column to the new array you made in 2(d). How many triangles are there now? _____

3. Use the array of squares to answer the questions below.

   a. _____ + _____ + _____ + _____ + _____ = _____

   b. _____ rows of _____ = _____

   c. _____ columns of _____ = _____

   d. Remove 1 row. How many squares are there now? _____

   e. Remove 1 column from the new array you made in 3(d). How many squares are there now? _____

EUREKA
MATH™

©2015 Great Minds. eureka-math.org
G2-M6-SE-B3-1.3.1-1.2016

Name _____   Date _____

1. Complete each missing part describing each array.

Circle rows.

a.

3 rows of _____ = _____

___ + ___ + ___ = _____

Circle columns.

b.

4 columns of _____ = _____

___ + ___ + ___ + ___ = _____

Circle rows.

c.

5 rows of _____ = _____

___ + ___ + ___ + ___ + ___ = ___

Circle columns.

d.

3 columns of _____ = _____

___ + ___ + ___ = ___

EUREKA MATH

Lesson 6:   Decompose arrays into rows and columns, and relate to repeated addition.

23

©2015 Great Minds. eureka-math.org
G2-M6-SE-B3-1.3.1-1.2016

2. Use the array of smiley faces to answer the questions below.

a. _____ rows of _____ = _____

b. _____ columns of _____ = _____

c. _____ + _____ + _____ = _____

d. Add 1 more row. How many smiley faces are there now? _____

e. Add 1 more column to the new array you made in 2(d). How many smiley faces are there now? _____

3. Use the array of squares to answer the questions below.

a. _____ + _____ + _____ + _____ = _____

b. _____ rows of _____ = _____

c. _____ columns of _____ = _____

d. Remove 1 row. How many squares are there now? _____

e. Remove 1 column from the new array you made in 3(d). How many squares are there now? _____

24   Lesson 6:   Decompose arrays into rows and columns, and relate to repeated addition.

EUREKA MATH

©2015 Great Minds. eureka-math.org
G2-M6-SE-B3-1.3.1-1.2016

Name _____   Date _____

1. a. One row of an array is drawn below. Complete the array with X's to make 3 rows of 4. Draw horizontal lines to separate the rows.

    <u>X X X X</u>

b. Draw an array with X's that has 3 columns of 4. Draw vertical lines to separate the columns. Fill in the blanks.

_____ + _____ + _____ = _____

3 rows of 4 = _____

3 columns of 4 = _____

2. a. Draw an array of X's with 5 columns of three.

b. Draw an array of X's with 5 rows of three. Fill in the blanks below.

_____ + _____ + _____ + _____ + _____ = _____

5 columns of three = _____

5 rows of three = _____

Lesson 7:   Represent arrays and distinguish rows and columns using math drawings.

©2015 Great Minds. eureka-math.org
G2-M6-SE-B3-1.3.1-1.2016

In the following problems, separate the rows or columns with horizontal or vertical lines.

3. Draw an array of X's with 4 rows of 3.

_____ + _____ + _____ + _____ = _____

4   rows of 3 = _____

4. Draw an array of X's with 1 more row of 3 than the array in Problem 3. Write a repeated addition equation to find the total number of X's.

5 Draw an array of X's with 1 less column of 5 than the array in Problem 4. Write a repeated addition equation to find the total number of X's.

Lesson 7:   Represent arrays and distinguish rows and columns using math drawings.

EUREKA MATH™

©2015 Great Minds. eureka-math.org
G2-M6-SE-B3-1.3.1-1.2016

Name _____   Date _____

1. a. One row of an array is drawn below. Complete the array with X's to make 4 rows of 5. Draw horizontal lines to separate the rows.

<u>X X X X X</u>

b. Draw an array with X's that has 4 columns of 5. Draw vertical lines to separate the columns. Fill in the blanks.

_____ + _____ + _____ + _____ = _____

4 rows of 5 = _____

6 columns of 5 = _____

2. a. Draw an array of X's with 3 columns of 4.

b. Draw an array of X's with 3 rows of 4. Fill in the blanks below.

_____ + _____ + _____ = _____

3 columns of 4 = _____

3 rows of 4 = _____

Lesson 7:   Represent arrays and distinguish rows and columns using math drawings.

27

©2015 Great Minds. eureka-math.org
G2-M6-SE-B3-1.3.1-1.2016

In the following problems, separate the rows or columns with horizontal or vertical lines.

3. Draw an array of X's with 3 rows of 3.

_____ + _____ + _____ = _____

3   rows of 3 = _____

4. Draw an array of X's with 2 more rows of 3 than the array in Problem 3. Write a repeated addition equation to find the total number of X's.

5. Draw an array of X's with 1 less column than the array in Problem 4. Write a repeated addition equation to find the total number of X's.

Lesson 7:   Represent arrays and distinguish rows and columns using math drawings.

©2015 Great Minds. eureka-math.org
G2-M6-SE-B3-1.3.1-1.2016

Name _____   Date _____

1. Create an array with the squares.

_____

_____

2. Create an array with the squares from the set above.

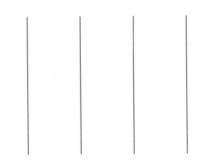

3. Use the array of squares to answer the questions below.

a. There are _____ squares in each row.

b. _____ + _____ = _____

c. There are _____ squares in each column.

d. _____ + _____ + _____ + _____ + _____ = _____

©2015 Great Minds. eureka-math.org
G2-M6-SE-B3-1.3.1-1.2016

4. Use the array of squares to answer the questions below.

    a. There are _____ squares in one row.

    b. There are _____ squares in one column.

    c. _____ + _____ + _____ = _____

    d. 3 columns of _____ = _____ rows of _____ = _____ total

5. a. Draw an array with 8 squares that has 2 squares in each column.

    b. Write a repeated addition equation to match the array.

6. a. Draw an array with 20 squares that has 4 squares in each column.

    b. Write a repeated addition equation to match the array.

    c. Draw a tape diagram to match your repeated addition equation and array.

EUREKA
MATH™

©2015 Great Minds. eureka-math.org
G2-M6-SE-B3-1.3.1-1.2016

Name _____   Date _____

1. Create an array with the squares.

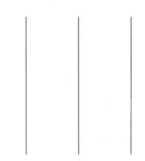

   _____

   _____

2. Create an array with the squares from the set above.

   | | |

3. Use the array of squares to answer the questions below.

   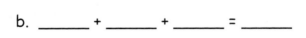

   a. There are _____ squares in each row.

   b. _____ + _____ + _____ = _____

   c. There are _____ squares in each column.

   d. ____ + ____ + ____ + ____ + ____ = ____

EUREKA MATH™

©2015 Great Minds. eureka-math.org
G2-M6-SE-B3-1.3.1-1.2016

4. Use the array of squares to answer the questions below.

   a. There are _____ squares in one row.

   b. There are _____ squares in one column.

   c. _____ + _____ = _____

   d. 2 columns of _____ = _____ rows of _____ = _____ total

5. a. Draw an array with 15 squares that has 3 squares in each column.

   b. Write a repeated addition equation to match the array.

6. a. Draw an array with 20 squares that has 5 squares in each column.

   b. Write a repeated addition equation to match the array.

   c. Draw a tape diagram to match your repeated addition equation and array.

Lesson 8:   Create arrays using square tiles with gaps.

EUREKA
MATH

©2015 Great Minds. eureka-math.org
G2-M6-SE-B3-1.3.1-1.2016

Name _____   Date _____

Draw an array for each word problem. Write a repeated addition equation to match each array.

1. Jason collected some rocks. He put them in 5 rows with 3 stones in each row. How many stones did Jason have altogether?

2. Abby made 3 rows of 4 chairs. How many chairs did Abby use?

3. There are 3 wires and 5 birds sitting on each of them. How many birds in all are on the wires?

4. Henry's house has 2 floors. There are 4 windows on each floor that face the street. How many windows face the street?

Lesson 9:   Solve word problems involving addition of equal groups in rows and columns.

33

©2015 Great Minds. eureka-math.org
G2-M6-SE-B3-1.3.1-1.2016

Draw a tape diagram for each word problem. Write a repeated addition equation to match each tape diagram.

5. Each of Maria's 4 friends has 5 markers. How many markers do Maria's friends have in all?

6. Maria also has 5 markers. How many markers do Maria and her friends have in all?

Draw a tape diagram and an array. Then, write a repeated addition equation to match.

7. In a card game, 3 players get 4 cards each. One more player joins the game. How many total cards should be dealt now?

Lesson 9: Solve word problems involving addition of equal groups in rows and columns.

EUREKA MATH™

©2015 Great Minds. eureka-math.org
G2-M6-SE-B3-1.3.1-1.2016

Name _____   Date _____

Draw an array for each word problem. Write a repeated addition equation to match each array.

1. Melody stacked her blocks in 3 columns of 4. How many blocks did Melody stack in all?

2. Marty arranged the desks in the classroom into 5 equal rows. There were 5 desks in each row. How many desks were arranged?

3. The baker made 5 trays of muffins. Each tray holds 4 muffins. How many muffins did the baker make?

Lesson 9:   Solve word problems involving addition of equal groups in rows and columns.

35

©2015 Great Minds. eureka-math.org
G2-M6-SE-B3-1.3.1-1.2016

4. The library books were on the shelf in 4 stacks of 4. How many books were on the shelf?

Draw a tape diagram for each word problem. Write a repeated addition equation to match each tape diagram.

5. Mary placed stickers in columns of 4. She made 5 columns. How many stickers did she use?

6. Jayden put his baseball cards into 5 columns of 3 in his book. How many cards did Jayden put in his book?

Draw a tape diagram and an array. Then, write a repeated addition equation to match.

7. The game William bought came with 3 bags of marbles. Each bag had 3 marbles inside. How many total marbles came with the game?

©2015 Great Minds. eureka-math.org
G2-M6-SE-B3-1.3.1-1.2016

Name _____ Date _____

Use your square tiles to construct the following rectangles with no gaps or overlaps. Write a repeated addition equation to match each construction.

1. a. Construct a rectangle with 2 rows of 3 tiles.

    _____

    b. Construct a rectangle with 2 columns of 3 tiles.

    _____

2. a. Construct a rectangle with 5 rows of 2 tiles.

    _____

    b. Construct a rectangle with 5 columns of 2 tiles.

    _____

EUREKA
MATH™

Lesson 10: Use square tiles to compose a rectangle, and relate to the array model.

37

©2015 Great Minds. eureka-math.org
G2-M6-SE-B3-1.3.1-1.2016

3. a. Construct a rectangle of 9 tiles that has equal rows and columns.

_____

   b. Construct a rectangle of 16 tiles that has equal rows and columns.

_____

4. a. What shape is the array pictured below? _____

   b. Redraw the above shape with one column removed in the space below.

   c. What shape is the array now? _____

Lesson 10:   Use square tiles to compose a rectangle, and relate to the array model.

EUREKA
MATH™

©2015 Great Minds. eureka-math.org
G2-M6-SE-B3-1.3.1-1.2016

Name _____   Date _____

Cut out the square tiles below, and construct the following arrays with no gaps or overlaps. On the line, write a repeated addition equation to match each construction on the line.

1. a. Construct a rectangle with
        2 rows of 4 tiles.

    b. Construct a rectangle with
        2 columns of 4 tiles.

    _____   _____

2. a. Construct a rectangle with
        3 rows of 2 tiles.

    b. Construct a rectangle with
        3 columns of 2 tiles.

    _____   _____

3. a. Construct a rectangle
        using 10 tiles.

    b. Construct a rectangle
        using 12 tiles.

    _____   _____

4. a. What shape is the array pictured below? _____

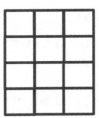

   b. In the space below, redraw the above shape with one more column.

   c. What shape is the array now? _____

   d. Draw a different array of tiles that is the same shape as 4(c).

©2015 Great Minds. eureka-math.org
G2-M6-SE-B3-1.3.1-1.2016

Name _____   Date _____

Use your square tiles to construct the following arrays with no gaps or overlaps. Write a repeated addition equation to match each construction.

1. a. Place 8 square tiles in a row.

    b. Construct an array with the 8 square tiles.

    c. Write a repeated addition equation to match the new array.

        _____

2. a. Construct an array with 12 squares.

    a. Write a repeated addition equation to match the array.

        _____

    c. Rearrange the 12 squares into a different array.

    d. Write a repeated addition equation to match the new array.

        _____

©2015 Great Minds. eureka-math.org
G2-M6-SE-B3-1.3.1-1.2016

3. a. Construct an array with 20 squares.

   b. Write a repeated addition equation to match the array.

       _____

   c. Rearrange the 20 squares into a different array.

   d. Write a repeated addition equation to match the new array.

       _____

4. Construct 2 arrays with 6 squares.

   a. 2 rows of _____ = _____

   b. 3 rows of _____ = 2 rows of _____

5. Construct 2 arrays with 10 squares.

   a. 2 rows of _____ = _____

   b. 5 rows of _____ = 2 rows of _____

Lesson 11:   Use square tiles to compose a rectangle, and relate to the array model.   EUREKA MATH

©2015 Great Minds. eureka-math.org
G2-M6-SE-B3-1.3.1-1.2016

Name _____   Date _____

1. a. Construct an array with 9 square tiles.

    b. Write a repeated addition equation to match the array.

    _____

2. a. Construct an array with 10 square tiles.

    b. Write a repeated addition equation to match the array.

    _____

    c. Rearrange the 10 square tiles into a different array.

    d. Write a repeated addition equation to match the new array.

    _____

Cut out each square tile. Use the tiles to construct the arrays in Problems 1–4.

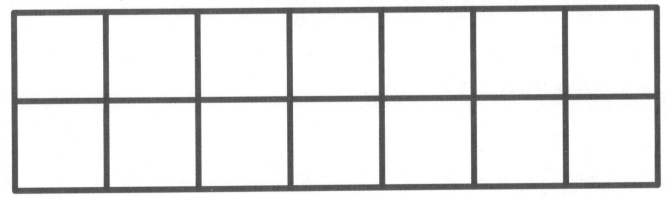

3. a. Construct an array with 12 square tiles.

   b. Write a repeated addition equation to match the array.

   _____

   c. Rearrange the 12 square tiles into a different array.

   d. Write a repeated addition equation to match the new array.

   _____

4. Construct 2 arrays with 14 square tiles.

   a. 2 rows of _____ = _____

   b. 2 rows of _____ = 7 rows of _____

Lesson 11:   Use square tiles to compose a rectangle, and relate to the array model.

EUREKA
MATH™

©2015 Great Minds. eureka-math.org
G2-M6-SE-B3-1.3.1-1.2016

Name _____   Date _____

1. Draw without using a square tile to make an array with 2 rows of 5.

2 rows of 5 = _____

_____ + _____ = _____

2. Draw without using a square tile to make an array with 4 columns of 3.

4 columns of 3 = _____

_____ + _____ + _____ + _____ = _____

©2015 Great Minds. eureka-math.org
G2-M6-SE-B3-1.3.1-1.2016

3. Complete the following arrays without gaps or overlaps. The first tile has been drawn for you.

   a. 3 rows of 4

   b. 5 columns of 3

   c. 5 columns of 4

Lesson 12:   Use math drawings to compose a rectangle with square tiles.

©2015 Great Minds. eureka-math.org
G2-M6-SE-B3-1.3.1-1.2016

Name _____ Date _____

1. Cut out and trace the square tile to draw an array with 2 rows of 4.

Cut out
and trace.

2 rows of 4 = _____

_____ + _____ = _____

2. Trace the square tile to make an array with 3 columns of 5.

3 columns of 5 = _____

_____ + _____ + _____ = _____

©2015 Great Minds. eureka-math.org
G2-M6-SE-B3-1.3.1-1.2016

3. Complete the following arrays without gaps or overlaps. The first tile has been drawn for you.

   a. 4 rows of 5

   b. 5 columns of 2

   c. 4 columns of 3

Lesson 12:   Use math drawings to compose a rectangle with square tiles.

EUREKA MATH™

Name _____   Date _____

Use your square tiles to complete the steps for each problem.

Problem 1

     Step 1: Construct a rectangle with 4 columns of 3.

     Step 2: Separate 2 columns of 3.

     Step 3: Write a number bond to show the whole and two parts. Then, write a repeated addition sentence to match each part of the number bond.

Problem 2

     Step 1: Construct a rectangle with 5 rows of 2.

     Step 2: Separate 2 rows of 2.

     Step 3: Write a number bond to show the whole and two parts. Write a repeated addition sentence to match each part of the number bond.

Problem 3

     Step 1: Construct a rectangle with 5 columns of 3.

     Step 2: Separate 3 columns of 3.

     Step 3: Write a number bond to show the whole and two parts. Write a repeated addition sentence to match each part of the number bond.

©2015 Great Minds. eureka-math.org
G2-M6-SE-B3-1.3.1-1.2016

4. Use 12 square tiles to construct a rectangle with 3 rows.

   a. _____ rows of _____ = 12

   b. Remove 1 row. How many squares are there now? _____

   c. Remove 1 column from the new rectangle you made in 4(b). How many squares are there now? _____

5. Use 20 square tiles to construct a rectangle.

   a. _____ rows of _____ = _____

   b. Remove 1 row. How many squares are there now? _____

   c. Remove 1 column from the new rectangle you made in 5(b). How many squares are there now? _____

6. Use 16 square tiles to construct a rectangle.

   a. _____ rows of _____ = _____

   b. Remove 1 row. How many squares are there now? _____

   c. Remove 1 column from the new rectangle you made in 6(b). How many squares are there now? _____

EUREKA
MATH

©2015 Great Minds. eureka-math.org
G2-M6-SE-B3-1.3.1-1.2016

Name _____   Date _____

Cut out and use your square tiles to complete the steps for each problem.

Problem 1

    Step 1: Construct a rectangle with 5 rows of 2.

    Step 2: Separate 2 rows of 2.

    Step 3: Write a number bond to show the whole and two parts. Write a repeated addition sentence to match each part of your number bond.

Problem 2

    Step 1: Construct a rectangle with 4 columns of 3.

    Step 2: Separate 2 columns of 3.

    Step 3: Write a number bond to show the whole and two parts. Write a repeated addition sentence to match each part of your number bond.

©2015 Great Minds. eureka-math.org
G2-M6-SE-B3-1.3.1-1.2016

3. Use 9 square tiles to construct a rectangle with 3 rows.

    a. _____ rows of _____ = _____

    b. Remove 1 row. How many squares are there now? _____

    c. Remove 1 column from the new rectangle you made in 3(b). How many squares are there now? _____

4. Use 14 square tiles to construct a rectangle.

    a. _____ rows of _____ = _____

    b. Remove 1 row. How many squares are there now? _____

    c. Remove 1 column from the new rectangle you made in 4(b). How many squares are there now? _____

©2015 Great Minds. eureka-math.org
G2-M6-SE-B3-1.3.1-1.2016

Name _____   Date _____

Cut out Rectangles A, B, and C. Then, cut according to directions. Answer each of the following using Rectangles A, B, and C.[1]

1. Cut out each row of Rectangle A.

    a. Rectangle A has _____ rows.

    b. Each row has _____ squares.

    c. _____ rows of _____ = _____

    d. Rectangle A has _____ squares.

2. Cut out each column of Rectangle B.

    a. Rectangle B has _____ columns.

    b. Each column has _____ squares.

    c. _____ columns of _____ = _____

    d. Rectangle B has _____ squares.

_____

[1]Note: This Problem Set is used with a template of three identical 2 by 4 arrays. These arrays are labeled as Rectangles A, B, and C.

©2015 Great Minds. eureka-math.org
G2-M6-SE-B3-1.3.1-1.2016

3. Cut out each square from both Rectangles A and B.

   a. Construct a new rectangle using all 16 squares.

   b. My rectangle has _____ rows of _____.

   c. My rectangle also has _____ columns of _____.

   d. Write two repeated addition number sentences to match your rectangle.

4. Construct a new array using the 24 squares from Rectangles A, B, and C.

   a. My rectangle has _____ rows of _____.

   b. My rectangle also has _____ columns of _____.

   c. Write two repeated addition number sentences to match your rectangle.

Extension: Construct another array using the squares from Rectangles A, B, and C.

   a. My rectangle has _____ rows of _____.

   b. My rectangle also has _____ columns of _____.

   c. Write two repeated addition number sentences to match your rectangle.

Lesson 14:   Use scissors to partition a rectangle into same-size squares, and
              compose arrays with the squares.

EUREKA
MATH™

©2015 Great Minds. eureka-math.org
G2-M6-SE-B3-1.3.1-1.2016

Name _____   Date _____

1. Imagine that you have just cut this rectangle into rows.

   a. What do you see? Draw a picture.

   How many squares are in each row? _____

   b. Imagine that you have just cut this rectangle into columns. What do you see?
      Draw a picture.

   How many squares are in each column? _____

2. Create another rectangle using the same number of squares.

   How many squares are in each row? _____

   How many squares are in each column? _____

Lesson 14:   Use scissors to partition a rectangle into same-size squares, and
             compose arrays with the squares.

55

©2015 Great Minds. eureka-math.org
G2-M6-SE-B3-1.3.1-1.2016

3. Imagine that you have just cut this rectangle into rows.

    a. What do you see? Draw a picture.

    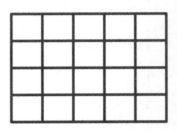

        How many squares are in each row? _____

    b. Imagine that you have just cut this rectangle into columns. What do you see?
        Draw a picture.

        How many squares are in each column? _____

4. Create another rectangle using the same number of squares.

    How many squares are in each row? _____

    How many squares are in each column? _____

Lesson 14:   Use scissors to partition a rectangle into same-size squares, and
                         compose arrays with the squares.

                                                                            EUREKA MATH

©2015 Great Minds. eureka-math.org
G2-M6-SE-B3-1.3.1-1.2016

Rectangle A

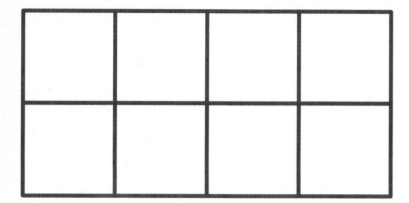

Rectangle B

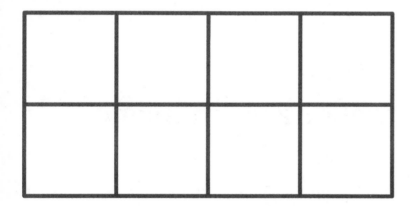

Rectangle C

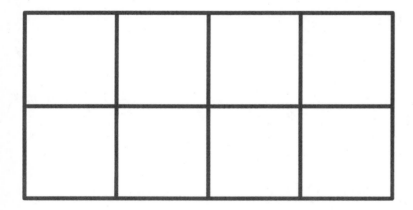

_____

rectangles

Lesson 14:   Use scissors to partition a rectangle into same-size squares, and
compose arrays with the squares.

©2015 Great Minds. eureka-math.org
G2-M6-SE-B3-1.3.1-1.2016

This page intentionally left blank

Name _____   Date _____

1. Shade in an array with 2 rows of 3.

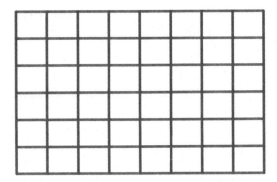

Write a repeated addition equation for the array.

_____

2. Shade in an array with 4 rows of 3.

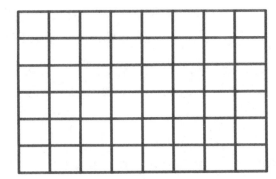

Write a repeated addition equation for the array.

_____

3. Shade in an array with 5 columns of 4.

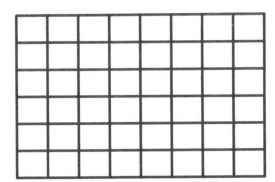

Write a repeated addition equation for the array.

_____

Lesson 15:   Use math drawings to partition a rectangle with square tiles, and relate to repeated addition.

59

©2015 Great Minds. eureka-math.org
G2-M6-SE-B3-1.3.1-1.2016

4. Draw one more column of 2 to make a new array.

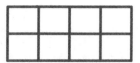

Write a repeated addition equation for the new array.

_____

5. Draw one more row of 4 and then one more column to make a new array.

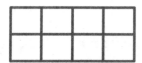

Write a repeated addition equation for the new array.

_____

6. Draw one more row and then two more columns to make a new array.

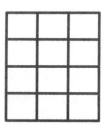

Write a repeated addition equation for the new array.

_____

©2015 Great Minds. eureka-math.org
G2-M6-SE-B3-1.3.1-1.2016

Name _____   Date _____

1. Shade in an array with 3 rows of 2.

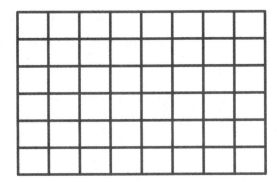

Write a repeated addition
equation for the array.

_____

2. Shade in an array with 2 rows of 4.

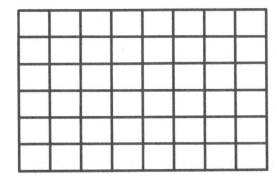

Write a repeated addition
equation for the array.

_____

3. Shade in an array with 4 columns of 5.

Write a repeated addition
equation for the array.

_____

Lesson 15:   Use math drawings to partition a rectangle with square tiles, and
              relate to repeated addition.

61

©2015 Great Minds. eureka-math.org
G2-M6-SE-B3-1.3.1-1.2016

4. Draw one more column of 2 to make a new array.

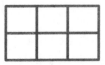

Write a repeated addition equation for the new array.

_____

5. Draw one more row of 3 and then one more column to make a new array.

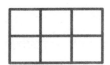

Write a repeated addition equation for the new array.

_____

6. Draw one more row and then two more columns to make a new array.

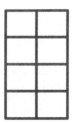

Write a repeated addition equation for the new array.

_____

Lesson 15:   Use math drawings to partition a rectangle with square tiles, and
                            relate to repeated addition.

©2015 Great Minds. eureka-math.org
G2-M6-SE-B3-1.3.1-1.2016

EUREKA
MATH

Name _____ Date _____

Use your square tiles and grid paper to complete the following problems.

Problem 1

   a. Cut out 10 square tiles.

   b. Cut one of your square tiles in half diagonally.

   c. Create a design.

   d. Shade in your design on grid paper.

Problem 2

   a. Use 16 square tiles.

   b. Cut two of your square tiles in half diagonally.

   c. Create a design.

   d. Shade in your design on grid paper.

   e. Share your second design with your partner.

   f. Check each other's copy to be sure it matches the tile design.

Problem 3

   a. Create a 3 by 3 design with your partner in the corner of a new piece of grid paper.

   b. With your partner, copy that design to fill the entire paper.

©2015 Great Minds. eureka-math.org
G2-M6-SE-B3-1.3.1-1.2016

Name _____ Date _____

1. Shade to create a copy of the design on the empty grid.

    a.

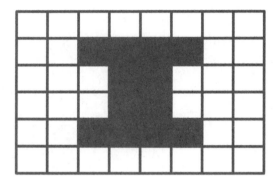 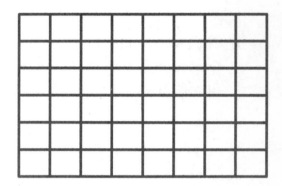

    b.

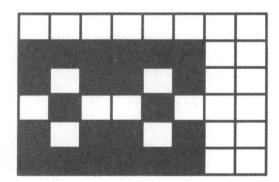 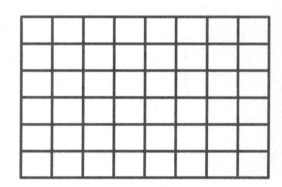

    c.

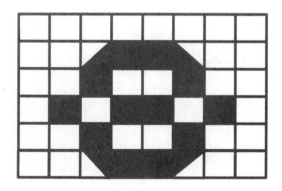 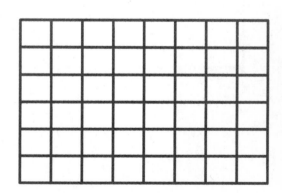

Lesson 16:   Use grid paper to create designs to develop spatial structuring.

EUREKA
MATH™

©2015 Great Minds. eureka-math.org
G2-M6-SE-B3-1.3.1-1.2016

2. Create two different designs.

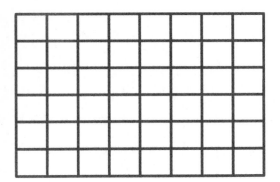 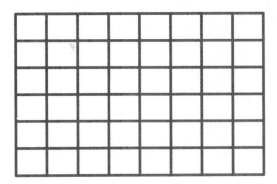

3. Use colored pencils to create a design in the bolded square section. Create a tessellation by repeating the design throughout.

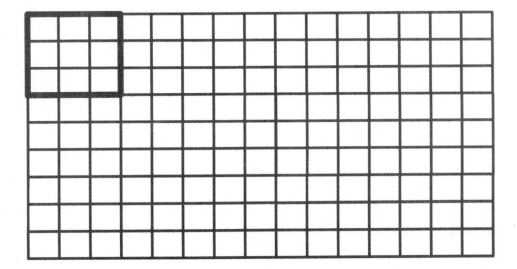

EUREKA
MATH™

©2015 Great Minds. eureka-math.org
G2-M6-SE-B3-1.3.1-1.2016

This page intentionally left blank

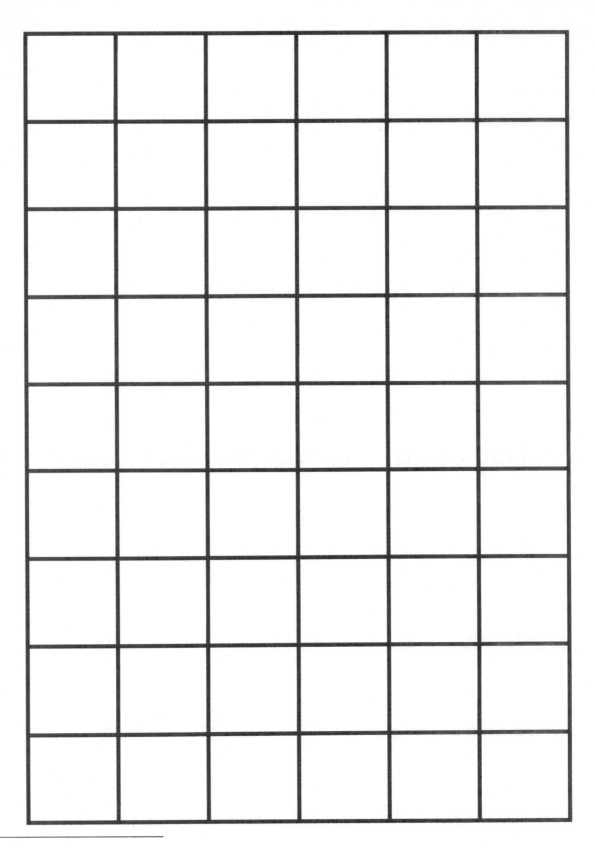

grid paper

©2015 Great Minds. eureka-math.org
G2-M6-SE-B3-1.3.1-1.2016

This page intentionally left blank

Name _____   Date _____

1. Draw to double the group you see. Complete the sentence, and write an addition equation.

a.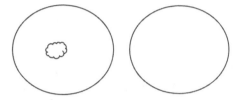

     There is _____ cloud in each group.

     _____ + _____ = _____

b.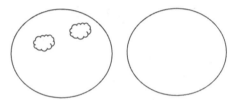

     There are _____ clouds in each group.

     _____ + _____ = _____

c.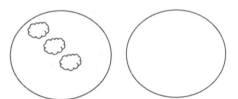

     There are _____ clouds in each group.

     _____ + _____ = _____

d.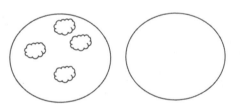

     There are _____ clouds in each group.

     _____ + _____ = _____

e.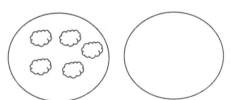

     There are _____ clouds in each group.

     _____ + _____ = _____

©2015 Great Minds. eureka-math.org
G2-M6-SE-B3-1.3.1-1.2016

2. Draw an array for each set. Complete the sentences. The first one has been drawn for you.

a. **2 rows of 6**

2 rows of 6 = _____

_____ + _____ = _____

6 doubled is _____.

b. **2 rows of 7**

2 rows of 7 = _____

_____ + _____ = _____

7 doubled is _____.

c. **2 rows of 8**

2 rows of 8 = _____

_____ + _____ = _____

8 doubled is _____.

d. **2 rows of 9**

2 rows of 9 = _____

_____ + _____ = _____

9 doubled is _____.

e. **2 rows of 10**

2 rows of 10 = _____

_____ + _____ = _____

10 doubled is _____.

3. List the totals from Problem 1. _____

List the totals from Problem 2. _____

Are the numbers you have listed even or not even? _____

Explain in what ways the numbers are the same and different.

Lesson 17:   Relate doubles to even numbers, and write number sentences to express the sums.

EUREKA MATH

©2015 Great Minds. eureka-math.org
G2-M6-SE-B3-1.3.1-1.2016

Name _____   Date _____

1. Draw to double the group you see. Complete the sentences, and write an addition equation.

a. 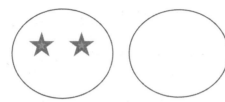   There are _____ stars in each group.

               _____ + _____ = _____

b. 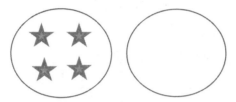   There are _____ stars in each group.

               _____ + _____ = _____

c. 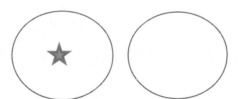   There is _____ star in each group.

               _____ + _____ = _____

d. 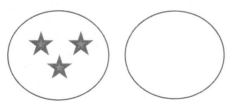   There are _____ stars in each group.

               _____ + _____ = _____

e.    There are _____ stars in each group.

               _____ + _____ = _____

©2015 Great Minds. eureka-math.org
G2-M6-SE-B3-1.3.1-1.2016

2. Draw an array for each set. Complete the sentences. The first one has been drawn for you.

   a. **2 rows of 6**

      2 rows of 6 = _____

      _____ + _____ = _____

      6 doubled is _____.

   b. **2 rows of 7**

      2 rows of 7 = _____

      _____ + _____ = _____

      7 doubled is _____.

   c. **2 rows of 8**

      _____ rows of _____ = _____

      _____ + 8 = _____

      8 doubled is _____.

   d. **2 rows of 9**

      2 rows of 9 = _____

      _____ + _____ = _____

      9 doubled is _____.

   e. **2 rows of 10**

      _____ rows of _____ = _____

      10 + _____ = _____

      10 doubled is _____.

3. List the totals from Problem 1. _____

   List the totals from Problem 2. _____

   Are the numbers you have listed even or not even? _____

   Explain in what ways the numbers are the same and different.

Lesson 17:   Relate doubles to even numbers, and write number sentences to
                                     express the sums.

                                                                                    EUREKA
                                                                                    MATH

©2015 Great Minds. eureka-math.org
G2-M6-SE-B3-1.3.1-1.2016

Name _____ Date _____

1. Pair the objects to decide if the number of objects is even.

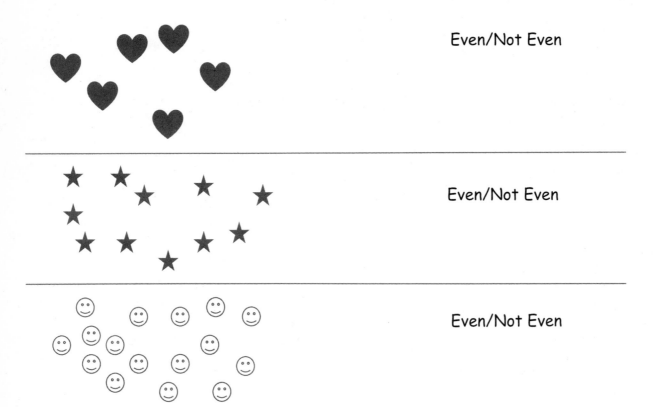

Even/Not Even

Even/Not Even

Even/Not Even

2. Draw to continue the pattern of the pairs in the space below until you have drawn 10 pairs.

EUREKA
MATH™

Lesson 18:   Pair objects and skip-count to relate to even numbers.

73

©2015 Great Minds. eureka-math.org
G2-M6-SE-B3-1.3.1-1.2016

3. Write the number of dots in each array in Problem 2 in order from least to greatest.

4. Circle the array in Problem 2 that has 2 columns of 7.

5. Box the array in Problem 2 that has 2 columns of 9.

6. Redraw the following sets of dots as columns of two or 2 equal rows.

   a.    b.

   There are _____ dots.   There are _____ dots.

   Is _____ an even number? _____   Is _____ an even number? _____

7. Circle groups of two. Count by twos to see if the number of objects is even.

   a. There are _____ twos. There are _____ left over.

   b. Count by twos to find the total.

   _____, _____, _____, _____, _____, _____, _____, _____, _____

   c. This group has an even number of objects: True or False

EUREKA
MATH™

©2015 Great Minds. eureka-math.org
G2-M6-SE-B3-1.3.1-1.2016

Name _____   Date _____

1. Pair the objects to decide if the number of objects is even.

   Even/Not Even

   Even/Not Even

   Even/Not Even

2. Draw to continue the pattern of the pairs in the spaces below until you have drawn zero pairs.

3. Write the number of hearts in each array in Problem 2 in order from greatest to least.

4. Circle the array in Problem 2 that has 2 columns of 6.

5. Box the array in Problem 2 that has 2 columns of 8.

6. Redraw the set of stars as columns of two or 2 equal rows.

    There are _____ stars.

    Is _____ an even number? _____

7. Circle groups of two. Count by twos to see if the number of objects is even.

    a. There are _____ twos. There are _____ left over.

    b. Count by twos to find the total.

        _____, _____, _____, _____, _____, _____, _____, _____

    c. This group has an even number of objects: True or False.

EUREKA
MATH™

©2015 Great Minds. eureka-math.org
G2-M6-SE-B3-1.3.1-1.2016

Name _____   Date _____

1. Skip-count the columns in the array. The first one has been done for you.

○ ○ ○ ○ ○ ○ ○ ○ ○ ○
○ ○ ○ ○ ○ ○ ○ ○ ○ ○

2 ___ ___ ___ ___ ___ ___ ___ ___ ___

2. a. Solve.

1 + 1 = _____

2 + 2 = _____

3 + 3 = _____

4 + 4 = _____

5 + 5 = _____

6 + 6 = _____

7 + 7 = _____

8 + 8 = _____

9 + 9 = _____

10 + 10 = _____

b. Explain the connection between the array in Problem 1 and the answers in Problem 2(a).

_____

_____

_____

©2015 Great Minds. eureka-math.org
G2-M6-SE-B3-1.3.1-1.2016

3. a. Fill in the missing numbers on the number path.

   20, 22, 24, _____, 28, 30, _____, _____, 36, _____, 40, _____, _____, 46, _____, _____

   b. Fill in the odd numbers on the number path.

   0, ____, 2, ____, 4, ____, 6, ____, 8 ____, 10, ____, 12, ____, 14, ____, 16, ____, 18, ____, 20, ____

4. Write to identify the **bold** numbers as even or odd. The first one has been done for you.

a.	b.	c.
6 + 1 = 7 <u>even</u> + 1 = <u>odd</u>	24 + 1 = 25 _____ + 1 = _____	30 + 1 = 31 _____ + 1 = _____
d. 6 – 1 = 5 _____ – 1 = _____	e. 24 – 1 = 23 _____ – 1 = _____	f. 30 – 1 = 29 _____ – 1 = _____

5. Are the **bold** numbers even or odd? Circle the answer, and explain how you know.

a.	**28** even/odd	Explanation:
b.	**39** even/odd	Explanation:
c.	**45** even/odd	Explanation:
d.	**50** even/odd	Explanation:

Lesson 19: Investigate the pattern of even numbers: 0, 2, 4, 6, and 8 in the ones place, and relate to odd numbers.

EUREKA MATH

©2015 Great Minds. eureka-math.org
G2-M6-SE-B3-1.3.1-1.2016

Name _____ Date _____

1. Skip-count the columns in the array. The first one has been done for you.

○ ○ ○ ○ ○ ○ ○ ○ ○ ○
○ ○ ○ ○ ○ ○ ○ ○ ○ ○

2 ___ ___ ___ ___ ___ ___ ___ ___ ___

2. a. Solve.

   1 + 1 = _____   6 + 6 = _____

   2 + 2 = _____   7 + 7 = _____

   3 + 3 = _____   8 + 8 = _____

   4 + 4 = _____   9 + 9 = _____

   5 + 5 = _____   10 + 10 = _____

   b. How is the array in Problem 1 related to the answers in Problem 2(a)?

   _____

   _____

   _____

3. Fill in the missing even numbers on the number path.

   18, 20, _____, _____, 26, _____ 30, _____, 34, _____, 38, 40, _____, _____

EUREKA
MATH

Lesson 19: Investigate the pattern of even numbers: 0, 2, 4, 6, and 8 in the ones place, and relate to odd numbers.

79

©2015 Great Minds. eureka-math.org
G2-M6-SE-B3-1.3.1-1.2016

4. Fill in the missing odd numbers on the number path.

0, _____, 2, _____, 4, _____, 6, _____, 8, _____, 10, _____, 12, _____, 14

5. Write to identify the **bold** numbers as even or odd. The first one has been done for you.

a.	b.	c.
4 + 1 = **5** <u>even</u> + 1 = <u>odd</u>	13 + 1 = **14** _____ + 1 = _____	20 + 1 = **21** _____ + 1 = _____
d. 8 – 1 = **7** _____ – 1 = _____	e. 16 – 1 = **15** _____ – 1 = _____	f. 30 – 1 = **29** _____ – 1 = _____

6. Are the **bold** numbers even or odd? Circle the answer, and explain how you know.

a. **21** even/odd	Explanation:
b. **34** even/odd	Explanation:

Lesson 19: Investigate the pattern of even numbers: 0, 2, 4, 6, and 8 in the ones place, and relate to odd numbers.

EUREKA MATH

©2015 Great Minds. eureka-math.org
G2-M6-SE-B3-1.3.1-1.2016

Name _____   Date _____

1. Use the objects to create an array.

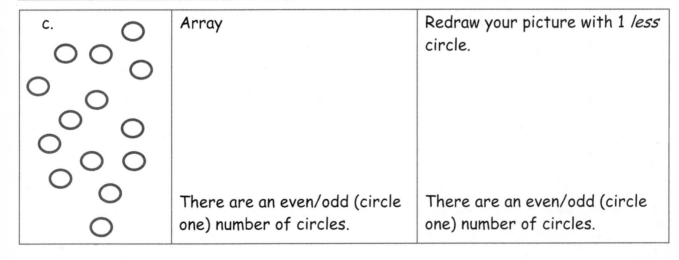

a.	Array	Redraw your picture with 1 *less* circle.
	There are an even/odd (circle one) number of circles.	There are an even/odd (circle one) number of circles.
b.	Array	Redraw your picture with 1 *more* circle.
	There are an even/odd (circle one) number of circles.	There are an even/odd (circle one) number of circles.
c.	Array	Redraw your picture with 1 *less* circle.
	There are an even/odd (circle one) number of circles.	There are an even/odd (circle one) number of circles.

©2015 Great Minds. eureka-math.org
G2-M6-SE-B3-1.3.1-1.2016

2. Solve. Tell if each number is odd (O) or even (E). The first one has been done for you.

a. 6   +   4   =   10   d. 14   +   8   =_____

___E___ + ___E___ = ___E___   _____ + _____ = _____

b. 17   +   2   =_____   e. 3   +   9   =_____

_____ + _____ = _____   _____ + _____ = _____

c. 11   +   13   =_____   f. 5   +   14   =_____

_____ + _____ = _____   _____ + _____ = _____

3. Write two examples for each case. Write if your answers are even or odd. The first one has been started for you.

a. Add an even number to an even number.

____32 + 8 = 40 even_____   _____

b. Add an odd number to an even number.

_____   _____

c. Add an odd number to an odd number.

_____   _____

©2015 Great Minds. eureka-math.org
G2-M6-SE-B3-1.3.1-1.2016

Name _____   Date _____

1. Use the objects to create an array with 2 rows.

a.	Array with 2 rows	Redraw your picture with 1 *less* star.
	There are an even/odd (circle one) number of stars.	There are an even/odd (circle one) number of stars.

b.	Array with 2 rows	Redraw your picture with 1 *more* star.
	There are an even/odd (circle one) number of stars.	There are an even/odd (circle one) number of stars.

c.	Array with 2 rows	Redraw your picture with 1 *less* star.
	There are an even/odd (circle one) number of stars.	There are an even/odd (circle one) number of stars.

©2015 Great Minds. eureka-math.org
G2-M6-SE-B3-1.3.1-1.2016

2. Solve. Tell if each number is odd (O) or even (E) on the line below.

a. 6 + 6 = _____   e. 7 + 8 = _____

_____ + _____ = _____   _____ + _____ = _____

b. 8 + 13 = _____   f. 9 + 11 = _____

_____ + _____ = _____   _____ + _____ = _____

c. 9 + 15 = _____   g. 7 + 14 = _____

_____ + _____ = _____   _____ + _____ = _____

d. 17 + 8 = _____   h. 9 + 9 = _____

_____ + _____ = _____   _____ + _____ = _____

3. Write three number sentence examples to prove that each statement is correct.

Even + Even = Even	Even + Odd = Odd	Odd + Odd = Even

Lesson 20:   Use rectangular arrays to investigate odd and even numbers.   **EUREKA MATH**

©2015 Great Minds. eureka-math.org
G2-M6-SE-B3-1.3.1-1.2016

4. Write two examples for each case. Next to your answer, write if your answers are even or odd. The first one has been done for you.

   a. Add an even number to an even number.

   _____32 + 8 = 40 even_____   _____

   b. Add an odd number to an even number.

   _____   _____

   c. Add an odd number to an odd number.

   _____   _____

©2015 Great Minds. eureka-math.org
G2-M6-SE-B3-1.3.1-1.2016

This page intentionally left blank